The Protein Crunch

Jason Drew and David Lorimer

First published in South Africa in 2011 by

Print Matters Planet

an imprint of
Publishing Print Matters (Pty) Ltd
P O Box 640, Noordhoek 7979, Western Cape, South Africa
info@printmatters.co.za
www.printmatters.co.za

A CIP catalogue record for this book is available at the South African Library.

Hard cover: ISBN 978-0-9869976-0-0
Soft Cover: ISBN 978-0-9869976-2-4
eBook: ISBN 978-0-9869976-3-1

Editorial Panel
Melissa Siebert and Robin Stuart-Clark

Cover Design
Katrin Hannusch and Kirsty Macfarlane

Book Design & Production
Stuart-Clark & Associates cc and Kirsty Macfarlane, Cape Town

Printing & Binding
MegaDigital, Cape Town
CTP Books, Cape Town
CPI Mackays, United Kingdom

MIX
Paper from
responsible sources
FSC
www.fsc.org   FSC® C020471

visit www.theproteincrunch.com

For our children

Jack and Charlie Drew, Charlotte and George Lorimer

ACKNOWLEDGEMENTS

This work brings together the detailed research of many international scientists and environmentalists who are too numerous to name and thank here individually. Without their inspiration and commitment to the environment the story of The Protein Crunch would not have been written.

We also acknowledge the very real suffering of the near one billion people who wake up hungry each day as a result of the environmental damage we have caused and the food system we have created.

Jason Drew and
David Lorimer – May 2011

CONTENTS

The credit crunch has shaken our global economy, but it will recover. 'The Protein Crunch' is far more serious and, if we open our eyes, it is unfolding right in front of us. Our food – protein – comes from three sources: our water, land and seas. All of these natural resources are under increasing pressure from our burgeoning population: when more demand meets less supply, we arrive at 'The Protein Crunch'.

Every day, newspapers cover some element of this looming issue: mine water pollution in Johannesburg, Chinese land purchases in the Congo, a single tuna sold for $380,000 in Tokyo, floods in Pakistan and the food price riots that ignited North Africa. Few of us understand the causes of these crises and events, nor how they are all connected. This book is the story of the crisis we face, from the viewpoint of an unashamed capitalist and entrepreneur. My belief is it will make you think; my hope is that it will make you act.

I have spent the last 25 years of my life fighting and winning in the game of business – from running other people's multinational companies to creating and then selling my own. Two heart attacks later, I realised that the only game worth playing was that of living. I changed the struggles of the boardroom for a passion for life and moved to live full time on my farm in South Africa's beautiful Tulbagh Valley.

I decided to walk myself fit. It turned out to be a journey of understanding of both the environment and myself. As the seasons changed I saw the streams dry up in summer and then flood in winter. Where we had felled trees, I saw soil erosion that turned the rivers muddy as they carried away the soil. This lit in me a passion and a concern for the environment: I began to read everything I could find on our water, land and seas.

I then travelled the world to see for myself the damage man is wreaking on these three vital eco-systems. I began to understand the extraordinary and unexpected connections between the many things I saw: from the teeming masses of China's cities to the fertile plains of the Indus Valley and the dry rivers of America's Mid-West – to name but a few. I began to realise the complexity of Nature and how the environment has shaped our past and will determine our future. During my travels over the last three years, two stories made an impact on me.

The first is a story of how wolves brought back the aspen trees to America's Yellowstone National Park. The aspen trees have always been a feature of its landscape, but the established trees were ageing and no new trees were replacing them. The last wolf in the park was shot in the 1920s, since when the elk population expanded rapidly and grazed on the young aspen saplings before they could grow and mature. Since the re-introduction of the wolves in 1995, the elk population has been reduced and their natural grazing habits have returned. The elk, frightened of the wolf packs, no longer graze at the river edges or in woods but on the open plains. Young sapling aspen trees now survive and as they mature the woodlands are naturally re-establishing themselves.

The second story is of a small island in the Bering Sea between Alaska and Russia. In 1944, a coastguard introduced 29 reindeer to the remote St Matthew Island as a reserve source of food for the men working there. The base was closed at the end of the Second World War, and all the men left the island. Just 13 years later, as they grazed on the abundant and nutritious lichen that covered much of the island, the reindeer population had reached 1,350. Without any natural predators on the island, the population exploded over the next six years, so that by 1963 there were 6,000 reindeer. But then disaster struck: the deer had eaten all the lichen, and just three years later there were only 42 left – 41 females, one sickly male and no fawns. This is a cautionary tale of what can happen when a species multiplies exponentially. In destroying their habitat, the reindeer destroyed themselves.

Just a 100 years ago it would have been inconceivable to think that the human impact on the environment might become so great as to threaten the Earth and our own survival. We now stand at a turning point in our history and in the history of the Earth. Mankind has acquired the scale and the power to wreck the biosphere on which we depend – yet also the knowledge to fix it. Throughout history, humans have cleared land or fished out rivers, and after exhausting other natural resources, moved on. Now with nearly seven billion people on the planet we are destroying environmental systems everywhere and simultaneously. There is nowhere else for us to go.

It is increasingly apparent that our capitalist global food system is not functioning effectively. With nearly one billion people hungry and another billion people overweight or obese, something clearly isn't working. Having watched the recent credit crunch unfold, I saw many similarities in the way our environmental and food production systems were and are being stretched to breaking point. With food demand outstripping supply, food prices will inevitably increase.

Food price inflation brings with it civil unrest and political turmoil, as we have witnessed in the first months of 2011. Social order has already started to collapse in many failed states like Sudan and Afghanistan. In our interconnected global world, state failure may become contagious as environmental refugees migrate to survive. Our civilisation is on the brink of disaster.

I decided to write the story of what I had seen with a family friend, environmentalist and author David Lorimer. The Protein Crunch explains our impact on the earth's natural systems and its resources on which we all depend. As some of these ecosystems become less productive or fail altogether, the speed and severity of 'The Protein Crunch' will accelerate. The way we respond to these environmental challenges is a matter of life and death, first for the poorest then for the rest of us, not to mention future generations. Many civilisations have collapsed before ours, but will we be the first to foresee our demise and prevent it?

It seems that our brains are wired to react to emergencies, but if the threat is not immediate we find it hard to galvanise ourselves into action. It is as if we are floating down a river heading towards a waterfall, ignoring the roar of the water and waiting until we see the foaming water, before we react and then look for someone else to blame for our predicament. What the Earth needs is for many more of us to understand our predicament, in order to change our collective consciousness and start the sustainability revolution we need to survive. There will be no time to waste looking for scapegoats: we will need to move and make change happen fast.

Capitalism may have caused many of our existing environmental problems, but the best way of making this change happen quickly is to use capitalism itself. As a lifelong capitalist and now eco-entrepreneur, I have seen and become involved with some extraordinary businesses around the world. Three of these are both unusual and interesting: using fly larvae, Gibraltar-based Agri-protein recycles abattoir waste into useable protein for animal feed at a fraction of the price of existing natural sources; the UK's Oxitec genetically modifies and breeds sterile male mosquitoes, which when released breed with wild females that lay eggs that won't hatch, substantially reducing disease-carrying mosquito populations; the Urban Wind Farm in Belgium has borrowed wind-accelerating techniques from aircraft wing construction as well as braking technology from Formula One racecars to help generate clean power from urban rooftops. All of these could be billion-dollar businesses within the next 10 years. The next Bill Gates and Mark Zuckerberg will make their fortunes in the business of the environment.

Before my journey into the environment, I understood neither the unbelievable risks we are running nor the extraordinary opportunities for entrepreneurs and eco-capitalists like myself. Commitment is the only thing that drives change. When you commit you act, and the world changes around you, conspiring to help you in ways you never thought possible. I am now committed full time to making a difference to the world we live in – through creating more awareness of the environment and excitement about the opportunities it can bring us all.

The clock is ticking. We are in a race between education and catastrophe. *The Protein Crunch* will help you understand the harsh reality of where we are and the exciting future we can make for ourselves.

Let's get busy repairing the future.

Jason Drew – May 2011
Tulbagh, Western Cape, South Africa

CHAPTER ONE – **WATER**

Water is the most extraordinary thing. There is as much water on the Earth now as when time began. You cannot make more, you cannot throw it away, you cannot destroy it. Water just is.

The drip of water from your kitchen tap could have been in the blood of a dinosaur or the sweat of a slave, the breath of an eagle or the gills of a fish. Water is endlessly recycled and is the only compound existing in Nature in all its three states: as a solid, a liquid and a vapour.

The Earth's surface is over 60% water – as are we. We can live for weeks without food but only days without water. Water has powered civilisations and caused their downfall. It has fuelled the industrial revolution, enabled the current population explosion and helped create our consumer goods – yet we take it for granted. We have to change the way we think about water: we need to understand and manage our scarce water resources before they manage us.

We are becoming increasingly aware of our daily household water usage, but most of us remain clueless about the amount of virtual water we use. Almost everything we eat or the goods we use require vast amounts of water to produce.

The water we use in our daily domestic activities is often metered and paid for making us more aware of its consumption. Households in the United Kingdom (UK) without a water meter use nearly 55,000 litres per person a year, or enough to fill more than two petrol tankers. Metered households use nearly 10,000 litres a year less. In Canada, amazingly, they manage to use five times more water than the UK of which more than half is used to irrigate their gardens.

17

In a typical industrialised country, 60% of water used inside the house is for bathing and flushing the toilet; 25% for laundry; and only 10% for cooking and cleaning. The trend in Europe and the United States (US) is to more efficient flushing systems, as mandated on all new builds. This could dramatically reduce our water, and therefore energy, consumption.

While we use a lot of water for bathing and flushing, we use almost as much in washing our clothes and linen. In the US top-loading washing machines are still used, rather than the front-loading European type designed to use 40% less water. The US and the rest of the world should mandate the use of front loaders as a first step towards saving water. New 'waterless' washing machine technologies would save both water in washing and energy in drying our clothes. Governments need to pave the way for these technologies by taxing the old technologies and subsidising the new.

Most of the Western world's water supply infrastructure is obsolete and requires repair, if not replacement. Imagine how much water is lost as a result of this poor maintenance and under-investment. In a water-scarce world, we need better solutions than the wasteful infrastructure upon which we currently depend.

When we waste water, we waste energy, causing pollution which can be avoided. The amount of energy required to produce and deliver clean water to households is substantial, and will increasingly feature in the cost of household water as energy prices rise

The minimum personal water requirement is around 50 litres a day, or roughly a third of what the average British household uses. In developing countries, a mere 20 litres per person per day is often

> **In a typical industrialised country, 60% of water used inside the house is for bathing and flushing the toilet; 25% for laundry; and only 10% for cooking and cleaning.**

considered a luxury. In the West water is increasingly provided by private companies focused on maximising short-term profit and not the public good. In developing countries, privatisation of water supply is pushed in return for loan and aid extensions. Many people in these poor countries do not yet have access to effective water supply, let alone sanitation, and often pay more for their water than the rich in the West.

The advent of the modern megacities and their associated slums has led to sanitation issues not seen in the West since pre-Victorian times. Consider the many millions of street dwellers in Mumbai without access to sanitation: half a kilogram of excrement per person per day equates to thousands of tons of human waste just left on the streets.

A possible solution could be waterless composting toilets as a key to water sustainability when we begin to provide sanitation to the developing world. These toilets are odourless and waterless systems that convert human waste into reusable compost for our fields. This modern technology confirms what we have always known: human waste is a great fertiliser.

The amount of water we use around the house may seem a lot, but it's nothing compared to the virtual water we consume indirectly through the food we eat and the things we buy. An invisible trade in virtual water underlies the world economy from agriculture to consumer goods.

It takes about 1,000 litres of water to grow a kilogram of grain. It can take 24 kilograms of grain to produce a kilogram of beef. It therefore takes a tanker load of water to make a kilogram of steak. The export of beef from the US to the Middle East is as much a trade in water as it is in protein or meat. If sufficient water existed in the Middle East it would grow its own cattle!

The sunlight that fell on the Earth millions of years ago – and on the Middle East in particular – was transformed and stored in the form of carbon. Trees or plankton that died became the carbon deposits that we know as coal and oil today. While the US is exporting condensed ancient underground water in the form of beef, the Middle East is exporting ancient condensed sunlight – both scarce and non-renewable resources.

Most of the fresh water available to us is used for agriculture. It takes 1,000 litres – or one tonne of water – to produce a glass of milk or 5,000 litres of water to make a kilogram of cheese. Much of the water used in irrigating our crops and animal feeds is pumped from natural underground reserves or aquifers. Rainfall on the plains above replenishes these water sources slowly, or never where they are 'fossil' or ancient trapped water deposits. It is estimated that America's Mid-West pumps more water out of its aquifers each year than has fallen in rain on the plains that fed them, since the time of Christ.

Nearly 800 million people live on food produced from currently unsustainable underground water sources. There are, however, beacons of hope: in Rajasthan's Alwar District in India – farmers have been drilling deeper and deeper in search of water to pump onto their fields in the dry season. The reintroduction – through pressure from the village elders – of smaller fields with multiple ridges to catch monsoon water has improved the local water dynamics. Instead of drilling their boreholes 10-12 metres deeper each year, farmers are now withdrawing them closer to the surface as the aquifers replenish. This traditional practise of `water containment' means that less topsoil gets washed away; water seeps back into the ground naturally to replenish the aquifer; and while much of the water evaporates, it falls again as rain. This provides a sustainable supply of water all year round, not just during the monsoon.

Few of us are aware of the water needed to make the goods we buy: for example, it took more than 30,000 litres of water to make your mobile phone. Water is needed to make most of its components – from the steel to the titanium, from the plastics to the glass and the packaging it comes in. The great dams in China are being built as much to feed its export industry as its agriculture.

A pair of denim jeans takes more than 10,000 litres of water to make, a cotton shirt almost half that. What about your wooden floorboards? Trees can consume up to 1,000 litres of water a day and will be decades old before they are made into something we walk on and take for granted. All around us we are condensing our precious water into the consumer products we use every day. Everything we eat and use is, in fact, a form of condensed or virtual water – even the water we drink takes water to produce.

The average person in Europe and the US uses about 4,000 litres of virtual water a day – as much as 20 times the amount of actual water we use around the house. This total water usage or our 'water footprint' combines both direct and indirect water use.

Everything we eat and use is, in fact, a form of condensed or virtual water – even the water we drink takes water to produce and clean it.

Water is not evenly distributed across the planet by location or time. In Britain people often complain that they have too much rain, yet more than a third of the world's population is already short of water. India, for example, gets almost all of its rain in huge, short downpours over a few months a year – its monsoon season. Five hundred million people live in countries with chronic water shortages. A further 2.4 billion people live in countries – mainly in Africa and Asia – where the water system is under stress.

Increased population and rising demand for water mean that by 2050, as many as four billion out of a projected world population of around nine billion will live in or migrate from countries chronically short of water. World demand for fresh water is expected to increase by 30%

between 2000 and 2030 as people eat more water-intensive foods, such as meat, and purchase more disposable consumer goods. This means that there will be less water available per person, particularly for the poor.

Almost all of the Earth's water is in its oceans; only 2.5% of its water is fresh. Of this fresh water, 75% is stored in ice sheets and glaciers, now melting, and just 10% in accessible underground aquifers. As much water again is locked away deep underground as ancient 'fossil' rainwater – water that is never replenished. Amazing as it might seem, only 0.3% of our fresh water is stored in lakes and rivers and even less than that in the soil and atmosphere.

We therefore have a finite supply of fresh water. Slightly more than a quarter of our fresh water is not locked in ice caps; this is the water available for our use. The natural process of evaporation constantly recycles this water as rainfall. Our clean water mainly comes from evaporation, where water vapour is transformed into clouds and then falls as rain, sleet or snow on land or sea. Some of the rain soaks into the ground; some seeps slowly into our aquifers. Most of the water flows downhill as run-off, eventually returning to the sea where the process begins again.

Water is constantly in circulation. The heat of the sun causes 500,000 cubic kilometres to evaporate annually. This is 50,000 times more water than there is in Loch Ness and 250,000 times more water than is stored in South Africa's Voelvlei dam. This water vapour makes up 60% of atmospheric gases. Any increase in temperature means that the atmosphere absorbs more moisture.

As the cycle continues, extreme weather events are more common, as we have seen in 2010-2011 – with floods in Pakistan and Australia and mudslides in Brazil. Floods spreading over a wide area also cause huge evaporation, as the shallow body of water warms more quickly than, for example, a deep, cool lake. This results in more water vapour in the atmosphere and even more rain. In this way one flood can lead to another.

Trees generate their own water and cause rain through evaporation. Clearing of areas like the once-proud cedar forests of the Lebanon has led to its desertification. Humanity is dramatically altering the nature of water and water flows. Deforestation is the consequence of man's demands for land and fuel, which have increased exponentially since the earliest civilisations, promoting both more floods and more droughts. The floods, often caused by deforestation, however, do not help replenish the groundwater and cause massive soil erosion, which in turn contributes to the creation of permanent deserts.

Clearance of forests and tree cover exposes the ground to the sun, which then heats and hardens it. Rain cannot easily penetrate hot, hard, dry soil. Warm ground creates a fast run-off of water which, in times of heavy rainfall, can result in catastrophic floods, as experienced recently in Pakistan. That so-called 'natural disaster' was, in fact, predominantly man-made.

In areas of natural forest with good tree cover, the soil is soft and cool and rain penetrates the moist soil. In established forest, as much as 85% of the rainfall is retained by either sinking into the ground, or through absorption by trees and other vegetation. Consequently, the level of groundwater and water tables are maintained, and water run-off and soil erosion are less.

A key function of tropical forests is to help create and recycle rain. Since the 1960s man has used chemicals to make clouds give up their water and make rain in target areas. Planes fly through clouds and release a chemical spray; the moisture in the cloud clings to these drops and the cloud releases its water as rain in a process known as 'seeding'. Based on ongoing research into Terpenes, organic compounds released by trees during photosynthesis, it seems that Nature has been cloud seeding for eons. Trees and forests cause rain through these compounds they release into the atmosphere.

Removing the natural forests, with their multiple tree species, short-circuits the complete water cycle with devastating results. Each tree species accesses water differently, both from the ground and the atmosphere. Broad-leaf trees will capture mist on their leaves, causing water to drop to the ground in greater volumes than slim-needled pine trees. A variety of mixed-wood trees in a rainforest will harness all the available forms

South Korea has reforested itself since 1950 – the world should follow its example.

of water from ground dew to mist and fog. The continuing destruction of rainforests will lead to further disruption of regional climate patterns, and so produce less rainfall. The only remedy is a massive, international tree-planting campaign.

Many of us are aware of the deforestation of the Brazilian rainforests and the campaigns to save them. We are far less aware of the African rainforests – equally enormous and important. These ecosystems are being destroyed, the forests felled with little regard for the environment and the wood shipped to China to fuel its manufacturing industries.

Like those of Tasmania, these African and Brazilian forests are being felled to produce wood pulp for the paper industry and to open up more grazing and agricultural land. Great strides have been made in the paper recycling industry: even the US – normally a laggard in green issues – has nearly tripled its rate of paper recycling to more than 55% in the last three decades. The Forest Stewardship Council (FSC) – an international non-governmental organisation (NGO) established in 1993 to promote responsible management of forests worldwide – is helping consumers purchase products from sustainable forest plantations, from which in time we may be able to satisfy most of our paper needs.

There are, of course, drawbacks with monoculture plantations of forests or crops. They are susceptible to disease and do not provide a natural habitat for the diverse wildlife that would inhabit a forest of mixed tree species.

Reforestation is possible and is happening on a surprising scale, with individual, local and even government commitment. South Korea, largely barren and devoid of trees in the 1950s, is now almost 65% forested and a great example of government leadership in reforestation. Turkey, cleared of many of its indigenous oak trees by successive wood-hungry empires, has undergone a radical one billion tree-planting campaign to reforest its marginal lands and prevent soil erosion and run-off. The acorns from these oak trees will once again be a source of protein for farm animals. This revolution in Turkey was inspired by two prominent businessmen, Hayrettin Karaca and Nihat Gokyigit. Spain has for centuries produced some of the most prized meats from animals fed on acorns.

In Niger, individual farmers facing drought and desertification have come up with their own version of reforestation. Many trees such as the invasive and non-indigenous wattle in South Africa and the acacias in north-west Africa are legumes, fixing nitrogen in the soil. By interspersing such trees on croplands the farmers increase natural fertilisation, provide shade to allow rain to penetrate the soil and prevent the soil from eroding during winds and floods.

Most of our fresh water is stored as ice and snow in the polar regions and in glaciers and snow caps in the world's mountain ranges. Fact: the snow caps and glaciers are disappearing. It does not matter whether this is the result of man-made global warming

25

or part of a natural warming cycle. This change will lead to a fundamental alteration in the water cycle, and humans, who depend on this cycle, will have to adapt – whether they like it or not.

Mount Kenya has been snow-capped for thousands of years, but photographs over the last 100 years record its rapid disappearance. It is likely that by 2040 it will be gone! Tanzania's Mount Kilimanjaro has lost 82% of its ice in the last century, of which 33% has disappeared over the last 20 years. 'Kili' may be ice-free as soon as 2015.

Rivers across the world that run all year round do so predominantly because of winter rainfall stored on mountain ranges as snow and ice and released by summer melting. Without these frozen reservoirs, we will face a different pattern of water availability which will affect our agricultural systems that rely on constant water flow. In addition, winter rainfall without being stored as snow, will rush unabated through river systems and cause devastation by flooding.

Take, for example, the Indus River that snakes through India and Pakistan to the sea: its constant flow of water is regulated by frozen reservoirs high in the Himalayas, as are many of China's rivers. This mighty river has been dammed and its water flow partially diverted along its length to provide irrigation for crops. The British built more kilometres of canals in Pakistan than they did railways in India to direct the waters of the Indus to irrigate Pakistan's once-dry but fertile plains. Access to water is already a source of tension between these two nuclear powers; what would happen to food production, electricity generation and industrial production if the Indus' summer flows were dramatically reduced? We have seen what happens when winter rainfalls are not stored: in August 2010, the resulting massive floods killed thousands of people and displaced millions as water flooded through the Indus Valley to the floodplains.

Many parts of the US are seeing changed weather patterns affecting rainfall, and reducing water availability. Reduced water supply combined with rising demand from an increasing number of users forewarns a crisis. Irrigation rights are often 'over-allocated', so that water rights allocated to different regions through which a river runs now exceed the amount of water flow in the river. This can cause local conflict in individual countries, but war in other parts of the world where countries share river systems, such as the Nile or the Jordan.

Montana in the US is home to Glacier National Park, containing more than 150 glaciers when first surveyed in the late 1800s. There are now just 35 glaciers, half already reduced in size due to melting, and many of these are forecast to disappear by 2030. This crisis will have a direct effect on the flow of the rivers from the park, and therefore on irrigated food production downstream.

It is not just agriculture that is affected by reduced glacial run-off into our rivers – the impact also hits river fish. Warm water contains less oxygen than cold water, and with less cold water entering the river, its temperature rises. Increased water temperature affects the river's ability to support a natural balance of aquatic life.

Significant initiatives across the world are seeking to improve and repair the water cycle. From reforestation projects in the 50 countries working with the FSC to land management in several Indian states to promote aquifer replenishment, and many other initiatives, organisations and individuals are engaged in repairing our natural water systems.

Our biggest single use of fresh water is for irrigation in agriculture. Developing countries have the highest agricultural water usage, but even variations of use within the European Union (EU) are striking. Countries like Greece and Spain, with the highest water consumption, are also the most prone to drought. Climate change – whether man-made or natural – is likely to bring severe drought conditions to many parts of Europe by 2080, especially in the south.

The same drought risk applies in many African countries, with rapid population expansion requiring ever more of their already scarce water supplies. In Somalia the population is expected to increase from 8.8 million in 2000 to 31.8 million by 2050; in Sudan the projected jump is from 31.1 million to 59.2 million. Both countries rely heavily on woefully inefficient open and flood irrigation systems to produce their food supply. Rather than directing the right amount of water to the crops when they need it, these systems tend to overuse water and allow considerable evaporation and leakage from the open canals used for water delivery. With their water supplies already under pressure, and without massive investment, countries like Sudan and Somalia will struggle to feed their growing populations.

Without irrigation we cannot feed the world. We are already using and wasting much of the fresh water we have. Only 25% of the water in our rivers reaches the sea, as it is abstracted by agriculture and industry before it gets there.

Many rivers – such as the Colorado and Rio Grande in the US, the Yellow River in China and the Indus in Pakistan – are no longer running as far as the sea or may not run there much longer. We were taught as children that all rivers end in the sea – with the exception of Botswana's Okavango. We may have to re-map our rivers and rewrite our geography books in the near future.

Our overuse of rivers and their altered flow rates in summer will create a crisis in irrigation for agriculture and in drinking water for cities. Although only 17% of the world's cropland (270 million hectares) is irrigated, this land area produces more than a third of the world's food. Irrigation uses a staggering 70% of all the water drawn from rivers and underground reserves. In China half of all cropland is irrigated, and this land produces 80% of its grain harvest. Of all irrigated farmland worldwide, 75% is in developing countries and 25% in industrialised countries.

Without irrigation we cannot feed the world. We are already using and wasting much of the fresh water we have. Only 25% of the water in our rivers reaches the sea, as it is abstracted by agriculture and industry before it gets there.

Open canal irrigation processes can be made far more efficient by introducing drip irrigation, where water is directed to the roots of plants. This method uses comparatively little water with less waste. It is, however, an expensive system that many developing country agricultural systems cannot afford.

After World War II many countries needed to maximise production and end food rationing. Guaranteed product prices combined with incentives to use nitrogen-based fertilisers increased investment in output. A new generation of hybrid agricultural crops, from cereals to vegetables, further increased farming output per hectare. Many high-yielding plants of this 'Green Revolution' are, however, water guzzlers. The latest generation of genetically modified (GM) crops is now being developed to be pest- and drought-resistant and to use less water per unit of output.

Twenty percent of our fresh water is used by businesses. The power generation, chemicals, as well as the metal and paper industries consume vast quantities of fresh water in providing our heat and light as well as consumer goods. It takes 95 litres of water to produce a kilogram of steel and 324 litres to manufacture a kilogram of paper. Demand for water will increase substantially as more countries industrialise, adding further pressure on overall supply.

Industrial production processes also pollute our water systems and groundwater. Industrial chemicals are discharged into rivers, lakes and aquifers – including heavy metals like lead, cadmium and mercury. The deadly toxic chemical spill in Hungary in October 2010 highlights the danger to life – human, animal and vegetable. Thousands of people were affected, with hundreds of injuries and eight deaths as a toxic sludge dam linked to an aluminium plant collapsed. A national state of emergency was declared. The effects will take decades to clear from the river and food systems – particularly from the Danube.

In 1996 a leak of 1.5 million cubic metres of mine waste in the Philippines killed wildlife in a 27-kilometre stretch of river and raised the level of zinc in drinking water to dangerous levels. Rising water levels in disused mines near the megacity of Johannesburg, South Africa, now threaten the drinking water of the city's more than 10 million residents. As the water fills up the deep, disused mineshafts, it becomes rich in poisonous minerals and metals from these mines. Once the water levels reach the water table the consequences could be disastrous. South African President Jacob Zuma and former Minister of Water and Environmental Affairs Buyelwa Sonjica may face criminal charges in their personal capacities following charges brought against them by Nicole Barlow, chair of the Environment & Conservation Association of South Africa.

Fresh, clean water supplies are vital to soft drink and beer producers. It takes nearly 150 litres of water to make a pint of beer and three litres of water to make a litre of Coke. If access to clean water diminishes, these producers are in trouble. South African-based SAB Miller, for instance – one of the world's largest brewers – uses huge quantities of water from the Johannesburg area to make its beer. With the rising water levels in local disused mines threatening to pollute the area's water table, production could be seriously affected. Similarly, in August 2006 both Coca-Cola and PepsiCo in India suffered reduced sales as it was feared that the water they were using to produce their soft drinks was contaminated with pesticides. Several states in India banned their sale.

The industrialisation of agriculture has necessitated an increasing use of chemicals in fertilisers and pesticides. These chemicals run off into rivers and lakes as well as leaching into the soil and contaminating drinking water. Run-off into lakes and the seas can lead to a massive explosion of algae and weeds. These plants can, in turn, absorb so much oxygen that they deprive fish of the oxygen they need to survive. The recent mass deaths of sardines off the Californian coast in March 2011 or in the Louisiana marshes in September 2010 are just two of many examples.

The Mississippi River in the US has become so polluted with agricultural chemicals and household detergents that a huge area of the Gulf of Mexico has become an ecologically dead zone, incapable of supporting fish or any other form of sea life. Where our rivers still reach the seas, more and more of these dead zones are appearing, some 415 already exist, in estuaries around the world.

Traditionally in Africa and elsewhere, small dams were constructed to store seasonal rain for local summer use by farmers and communities. These usually have little impact on the environment. Damming of major rivers, however, has already harnessed and diverted 60% of the world's river waters for hydro-electric power, irrigation schemes and flood control. There are nearly 50,000 dams in the world, nearly half of which are in China.

The huge megastructure dams of the last 100 years have wreaked the most environmental devastation. Cumulatively, it is estimated that a staggering 80 million people worldwide have been relocated to facilitate controlled river valley flooding and dam construction, the most recent being the Three Gorges Dam across the Yangtze River in China. Since its construction began in 1994, the dam has displaced 1.2 million people, and upon completion in 2009 it had flooded 400 square miles of farmland.

The impact on fish, wildlife and plants, the reduction in fertile farming land along riverbanks and the hidden cost of damaging poorly understood ecosystems are immense. Forty percent of irrigated cropland relies on water supplied from dams, while hydro-electric power stations generate 20% of the world's electricity. These power stations, like all power stations, also use massive amounts of water for cooling their turbines.

Environmentalists have long been highlighting the destruction caused by large dam projects. More recently they have been joined by the World Bank, which since 1948, has spent around US$75 billion on dam projects in more than 90 countries. Many of these projects have delivered substantially less than they promised in terms of hydro-electric power, water supply and flood protection.

All too often, however, these dams are built in areas where the rivers are already muddy with topsoil eroded through deforestation. Silt builds up behind the dam walls, eventually reducing storage capacity; by preventing the flow of silt downstream, the fertility of floodplains is reduced while riverbanks are eroded. Some of these immense projects have a life expectancy of only 100 years or so before they are left as a valley full of dangerous silt – a lethal mud tsunami waiting to happen.

In times of excessive rainfall, and where reservoirs are already full, operators occasionally have to make large emergency releases of water, thus causing the very floods that dams are designed to prevent. Overall, the benefits of dams flow mainly to townspeople, while the impact of these projects falls most heavily on the rural poor, whose fields are flooded and rivers and wetlands spoiled.

The sheer scale and extent of some water diversion and dam projects contribute to the number of major rivers no longer reaching the sea. To help understand the volumes of water we are talking about: one cubic kilometre of water is the same as 350,000 public swimming pools full of water, or more than a bath full for every man, woman and child on the planet.

Only a century ago, 25 cubic kilometres of water a year flowed down the Colorado River straight into the Gulf of California. The Colorado River supplies seven states and Mexico, and water rights have been regulated since 1922 when a total of 20.5 cubic kilometres was allocated between its users. Since this agreement was signed, the average flow has fallen to 16 cubic kilometres. From 1999 to 2003 the average flow was only half that at 8.7 cubic kilometres, with 2002 providing the lowest flow of a mere 3.7 cubic kilometres. Most of this water is diverted upstream, for agricultural use. It is clear that this situation is totally unsustainable, especially in the light of rising demand from the cities that border the river.

The decline and death of the Aral Sea in Kazakhstan is perhaps the most catastrophic result of water diversion from the Amu Darya and Syr Darya rivers. Almost the entire flow of these two giant rivers – 110 cubic kilometres a year – was diverted in order to grow cotton in the desert. Until the 1960s, the Aral Sea was as large as the countries of Belgium and the Netherlands combined. The sea contained more than 1,000 cubic kilometres of water, with a reputation for its blue waters, picturesque beaches and busy fishing ports with an annual catch of 60,000 tonnes of fish.

Now, 50 years later, the Aral Sea has been reduced to three salt-saturated expanses, containing 10% of the sea's original water volume. The sea's fish have long since died, and its ports and beaches have been abandoned – some of these former ports are now more than 50 kilometres from the water. The area covered with water has reduced by two-thirds, exposing vast moonscape-like tracts of land.

The last 10 years have, however, seen a remarkable recovery as flows from the Syr Darya River have been restored. This raised local water levels by three metres, which was enough to begin reviving fisheries. This is a real sign of hope that determined restoration effects can reverse some ecological collapses.

The near-disappearance of the Aral Sea, a man-made disaster on an unprecedented scale, has also changed the area's climate. The sea used to facilitate rainfall and moderate the temperature, creating cooler summers and warmer winters. The summers are now three degrees hotter, winters colder and longer, and cotton has to be planted in May rather than March.

The near-disappearance of the Aral Sea, a man-made disaster on an unprecedented scale, has also changed the area's climate.

The Murray River Basin in southern Australia is another disaster area, where thousands of giant gum trees have been cleared. Replacing trees with irrigated crops results in rising water tables, since there are no trees to use and breathe the groundwater into the atmosphere. As the water table rises, it brings deep water nearer the surface and with it billions of tonnes of minerals and salt. This mineral-rich or salinated water is rendering the soil infertile. The same effect is seen throughout the world where deep groundwater sources are used for irrigation. It is ironic that rice, cotton and sugar account for a third of Australia's water use, and that a country short of water is actually an exporter of virtual water.

The Henley-on-Todd Regatta, held annually in the renowned Australian town of Alice Springs, is yet another classic example of a river no longer flowing except in flood. For the last 50 years, men have paraded in bottomless canoes in the Todd's dry riverbed as a parody of the Henley Royal Regatta on Britain's river Thames. The Henley-on-Todd is the only regatta to have been cancelled because of wet weather – in 1993 there was water in the river!

Water in underground aquifers gradually accumulates over centuries through water seeping into the ground. Aquifer water represents a form of slowly renewable capital, but in many places this water is being withdrawn much faster than it is being replaced. Groundwater is also the only form of drinking water available to about a quarter of the world's population, especially in cities. In the US, this percentage is 51%, while in Europe it reaches 75%.

Sanaa, the capital of Yemen, may become the first capital city in living memory to move because of a water shortage. The wells tapping the aquifer beneath the city are now as much as 1,000 metres deep and running on empty. Sanaa is likely to be a ghost city within the next decade. Across Yemen, Nature cannot replenish the aquifers fast enough to keep pace with the demands of a population set to double over the next 20 years. Local, often violent, skirmishing between water users is already common. The population will have to migrate from the mountains down to the coastal plains and look to desalinated water as an alternative supply – or more likely become water refugees in other countries.

The real problem globally is overuse of groundwater for irrigation. India, China and Pakistan pump out around 400 cubic kilometres of underground water a year, representing half the world's total use of underground water for agriculture. This rate of extraction exceeds the volumes of rainwater recharging those aquifers by somewhere between 150-200 cubic kilometres a year.

The result is a catastrophic fall of water tables. In Shanxi Province, China and beneath Beijing, the water table has fallen more than 70 metres. In Gujarat, India, a local water table is 150 metres down and is falling by a further six metres per year. Falling water tables have also led to land subsiding or sinking in parts of China and in Mexico. This can lead to the destruction of housing and civil infrastructure.

With diminishing underground water, farmers have to drill more boreholes and deeper every year – 21 million of them have been sunk in India alone over the last 20 years at a cost of US$12 billion. Worldwide we are critically vulnerable, with almost one billion people currently eating food grown using the unsustainable extraction of

35

groundwater. We are effectively living on borrowed time in the form of borrowed water. Even in the US, a third of its irrigation water comes from underground sources.

Water carries life, but it can also carry death. It is a continuing scandal that more than one billion people still do not have access to a safe supply of fresh, clean water. Research indicates that 2.3 billion people suffer from diseases linked to water. In developing countries this translates into 80% of all illnesses being water-related. Two hundred people an hour – more than 1.7 million a year – die as a result of unsafe water and sanitation.

Those of us who can simply turn on a tap can easily forget the many people who, several times a day, have to walk long distances to fetch and carry their water in containers. On average, these people use five litres a day, just sufficient for drinking and cooking but inadequate for the other uses most of us take for granted.

Untreated sewage leads to outbreaks of infectious diseases. In developing countries only a small amount of wastewater from sewage systems is properly treated, with most of it discharged straight into rivers, lakes and the sea. Many infectious diseases, like dysentery, cholera, typhoid and polio, are transmitted in drinking water contaminated by human or animal faeces. Children are particularly susceptible to diarrhoea, which can kill them through dehydration if nothing else. Disease can also be transmitted in water used to grow food crops.

In the 1970s, many boreholes were installed in Bangladesh in order to provide non-contaminated drinking water in an area where 250,000 people were dying every year from water-borne diseases. These wells were mainly sunk to depths of between 20 and 100 metres, where it turned out that the water was contaminated by arsenic carried by underground water from deposits in the foothills of the Himalayas.

In developing countries only a small amount of the wastewater from sewage systems is properly treated, with much of it discharged straight into rivers, lakes and the sea.

Consequently, some 12 million backyard wells contained poisoned water.

An insidious epidemic is creeping up on these Bangladeshi villages, as it typically takes 10 years for symptoms such as skin lesions and cancers to appear. The World Health Organisation (WHO) calls this the largest mass poisoning of a population in history, and tragically the Bangladeshi government has been slow to respond, leaving tens of thousands of people still at material risk.

In New York City, at the other end of the wealth scale, drinking water is no less important. A coalition of committed individuals, government, forestry departments, national parks and water management has come together to protect the watershed that provides the city with its drinkable water. From purchasing land to altering farming practices and reforesting the land, the city has come together to protect and create sustainability in its single most important life support system – water.

Whether man-made or not, global warming means that there will be more moisture in the atmosphere. This translates into heavier and more frequent downpours in temperate climates like Britain, and more extensive flooding in others as we have seen across the southern hemisphere in 2010: what goes up must come down!

The drought in Northern Spain in 2007 and fires in Greece in 2009 are ominous signs of things to come for Europe. Consider that Europe's heat-wave summer of 2003 represented less than a one-degree average variation on long-term average temperatures. A climate warmed by three degrees will have a devastating effect on not just agriculture but also on viticulture. In parts of France like Bordeaux and Alsace, warmer temperatures, up by over a degree in the last 30 years, already mean that grapes have more sugar and therefore higher alcohol levels, and consequently the character of these wines will change.

Nearly 500 million people rely on the water flows of the Indus and the Ganges, fed by glacial melt water from the Himalayas. Many glaciers in the Himalayas are melting rapidly, and some could disappear completely by 2035. The giant Gangotri Glacier in northern India supplies 70% of the Ganges flow during the dry season, and if it disappears, the Ganges will become a seasonal river which could cease to flow during the summer when water need for irrigation is greatest. Without this water, very little irrigation will be possible, and even more groundwater – already being over-extracted – will have to be used.

The same applies to the glaciers feeding the Yangtze and Yellow rivers in China. The Yellow River Basin is home to nearly 150 million people, and their fate is closely tied to that of the river because of low rainfall in the basin. The Yangtze is China's leading source of surface irrigation water, and helps to produce around half of China's rice harvest. These impending water shortages will restrict river-based irrigation, and subsequently lead directly to shrinking harvests.

In 2008 water supply issues in India affected production and, combined with ever-increasing demand, led the Indian government to retain part of its rice exports and to import wheat for the first time. The threat that changing water cycles pose to our industrial food production systems is likely to lead to conflict and fuels the risk of wars in the future.

Overall, water scarcity exacerbated by climate change is expected to reduce global food production by 350 million tonnes a year by 2025, equivalent to the current grain harvest of the US. Furthermore, the 3.2 billion people added to the world's population by 2050 will mainly be born in countries already facing water scarcity – and because 40% of the world's food supply comes from irrigated land, water scarcity means food insecurity.

The major storage system for fresh water outside the Himalayas is in the polar regions. Climate change in the Arctic is faster than anywhere on the planet, as the pollutants covering the once-bright, white snow no longer allow sunlight to be reflected back into space.

The North Pole is now ice-free in summer and the northern sea route to the East is navigable. Robert Swan, the British polar explorer, commented in 2010 that he was the first person to walk to both Poles and may be the last. Fifty years ago the ice of the Arctic Sea was nearly two metres thick, but by 2001 this had halved. Overall, the ice sheet has thinned as well as shrunk in area by 6%. The loss through thinning is, in fact, far greater than the loss in area and disguises the scale of this development.

The long-term trend is clear – the Arctic is melting. It is not unprecedented and has happened before, but it made the world a very different place. Despite some recent short-term stabilisation and a decline in the rate of melting, the long-term trend is currently irreversible and inevitable. Since the ice shelf reflects back 70% of the sun's radiation while open water reflects only 6%, this melting creates more melting as less sun is reflected, so temperatures rise, and so on in a continuous downward spiral. This is compounded by pollutants covering the snow causing it to reflect less heat back to space.

The ice cap and glaciers of Greenland are also melting at an unprecedented rate, creating immense lakes of fresh water. If too much

39

of this water escapes into the Atlantic Ocean, it could shut down the already slowing Gulf Stream. This would have a dramatic effect on the world's climate, particularly that of Britain, which is directly moderated by the Gulf Stream. This moderation results in warmer winters and cooler summers than those of its continental neighbours on the same latitude.

More than 260 river basins are international, and 13 of these are shared by five or more countries. As many as 17 countries share the waters of the Danube. It's easy to see how disputes arise over the amount of water each country takes from shared rivers, or stores for itself in dams. There are currently many more positive interactions between countries on water issues than there are conflicts, including an international agreement between India and Pakistan over the Indus River.

Population growth and the corresponding increasing demand for water mean that disputes over river water are increasing. Downstream countries are more vulnerable and can object to plans proposed by upstream neighbours. The waters of the Nile are shared among Egypt, Sudan, Ethiopia, Uganda, Kenya and Rwanda. Treaties brokered by Britain in 1929 and 1959 gave Egypt and Sudan 90% of the water and a veto over any attempt by the countries nearer the source to divert water for their own use.

Egypt is wholly dependent on the lifeline of the Nile, without which it could not support its population, expected to rise from 68 million in 2000 to 114 million in 2050. Not surprisingly, Egypt regards its water supply as a security issue and has traditionally used military threats to maintain control over the Nile. This could be catastrophic for Ethiopia where 80% of the water of the Nile originates.

Ethiopia suffers from a chronic lack of water for its crops, which has condemned nearly 60% of its people to near-starvation. Its population –

as, ironically, with most populations facing poverty – is expected to increase rapidly. All the countries bordering the Nile face soaring populations: within 15 years there will be almost 800 million people in the Nile basin. Where more meets less, there is inevitably a recipe for conflict over limited water resources.

Water has already been the cause of armed conflict in modern times between Israel and its neighbour Jordan. Water is the most important resource throughout the Middle East. The Six-Day War in 1967 was largely a response by Israel to Jordan's proposal to divert the river Jordan for its own use. The land seized by Israel gave it access to the headwaters of the Jordan, and also control over the aquifer beneath the West Bank. This increased Israel's water resources by nearly 50%. Israel currently extracts up to 75% of the flow in the Jordan River, leaving only the remainder to reach the West Bank. As a result many Palestinians living there are forced to survive on as little as 35 litres a day. Water levels in both the Sea of Galilee and the Dead Sea are falling as the river flow is diverted by man. There are now plans to pump seawater to the Dead Sea to maintain its levels and preserve its ecosystem.

Water is often used as a weapon of war, with the deliberate destruction of dams, pipelines and the contamination of drinking water.

Water is often used as a weapon of war, with the deliberate destruction of dams, pipelines and the contamination of drinking water. Examples include terrorists threatening to blow up a dam in Tajikistan in 1998; Iran diverting water to flood the Iraqi defence positions in the 1980-1988 Iran/Iraq war; Bosnian Serbs poisoning water supplies in Sarajevo in 1992; and Saddam Hussein's army poisoning and draining the Tigris-Euphrates river estuary to dislodge the Marsh Arabs in coastal Iraq.

41

Our supply and use of water is a challenge that will only intensify over the next 20 years. We need a 'Blue Revolution' to follow on from the green or agricultural revolution of the '60s and '70s to help us manage water before it manages us. The World Water Council's projections of water usage in 2025 make it clear that a 'business as usual' approach will simply make a bad situation even worse, as agricultural, industrial and domestic demand continues to expand in line with our rising population.

Our Blue Revolution needs to start now, with cutting out unnecessary and wasteful domestic water use. The water we do have will have to be used and reused, including the use of urban wastewater and short-interval water recycling. Carving up our fields once again with hedgerows and harnessing monsoons and other highly seasonal water with smaller-scale, farm-level dams and storage systems will help moderate the effects of the changing water flow patterns. This will not only help reduce soil erosion, but also help replenish our aquifers.

We need to allow and encourage the next generation of genetically modified water-wise crops to be developed without the anti-GM sentiment so easily generated in the developed West. World Bank

We react to crises as they arise – without taking the necessary action to avoid them.

funding must be diverted from funding dam construction to helping smaller-scale farmers at national-level move to drip irrigation systems.

We should all take note of the reforestation success stories and emulate them in many more countries. We need to achieve globally, and in a far shorter time span, what they have achieved quietly over the last 50 years.

The British government announced plans in February 2011 to sell off the state-owned forests. The politicians completely misread public sentiment, however, and did a complete turnaround when they realised the massive public opposition. More than 500,000 people signed an online petition, and with both celebrity and press support the proposal was scrapped. This once again shows that people, not their governments, will drive the change we need to save the planet – ecosystem by ecosystem.

Despite limited and weak political will, there is ongoing powerful environmental action driven by ordinary people – people like us. We can all make a difference, no matter how small, by acting right now. It's as simple as turning off the dripping garden tap. It is likely that we will end up on a path to sustainability not because of our governments, but despite them.

CHAPTER TWO – **LAND**

When we talk about land, particularly farmland, what we really mean is the relatively thin layer of soil that covers our rocky planet in patches and supports life as we know it. Soil is formed from the weathering of rocks into rock particles combined with organic matter from decaying plants. This soil then retains water and promotes plant growth which helps prevent erosion.

During the ice ages, glaciers scooped minerals and rocks from underground and mixed these with organic matter on the surface, creating much of the nutrient-rich soil that prompted an explosion of plant life. As the glaciers receded, more topsoil was created through plant decay, leaving us with a fertile, abundant planet.

Soil takes centuries to accumulate. Think of a huge pile of leaves in your garden left for the winter to break down and rot, or the straw mulch around your roses. A large pile of biodegradable matter makes only thimblefuls of compost: this is how long it takes for Nature to make soil. Soil is formed at a rate of 2.5 centimeters every 250-1,200 years, depending on climate, plant cover and local geology. It can take between 3,000 and 12,000 years to build up enough soil to make cultivatable land.

The depth of soil coverage varies enormously because it is created, moved and destroyed by glaciers, wind, rain and, most recently, man. Rain naturally moves some soil from wooded hillsides down to lower ground, creating fertile valleys and floodplains.

This slow accumulation process means that soil is created on an almost geological time scale. Without soil mankind cannot survive: soil is a non-renewable, finite resource that we must maintain and preserve for future generations.

45

Soil has three basic aspects: its physical structure, its chemical content and its biological activity. These three elements are intricately interconnected. The physical structure and therefore quality of soil depends on the proportions of organic and inorganic material in its composition – varying, for example, from soils that are mostly sand to purely organic material like peat. The mineral content in soil determines its nutritional quality and that of the plants growing in it. The biological activity in the soil – the patterns of life it sustains – is the most complex and least understood of its three facets.

Soil is unlike any other natural resource that humans use. It is neither an industrial component nor some inert resource to be exploited like an extracted mineral. It is alive and constantly changing, pulsating with organisms that thrive on its organic content. It is this life that makes it soil and not lifeless sand.

Over a decade that same hectare would be covered with worm casts just over five centimeters deep.

Living naturally in all our soil are nematodes – what we could call worms – tube-like creatures with a digestive tract. We don't know how many species of nematodes exist in Nature; some 30,000 species have been identified to date. Nematodes range in size from those that are invisible to the eye to the common earthworms we often find in our gardens. Each cubic metre of soil contains up to 10 million nematodes – or 10,000 in an average plant pot.

As nematodes work, they ingest and churn the earth, breaking down and distributing organic matter from the surface throughout the topsoil. On a single hectare nematode or worm casts can bring an astonishing 25 tonnes of soil a year to the surface. Over a decade that same hectare would be covered with worm casts just over five centimeters deep. These droppings are rich in nitrogen, calcium, magnesium and phosphorus, all important nutrients for healthy soil and agriculture.

By tunnelling through the soil, nematodes provide passageways through which air, water and nutrients can circulate and help prevent soil compaction. This is important because soil microorganisms and plant roots need air and water which together nourish the plant. Traditional farming methods involve ploughing the land, scattering seeds, and then covering them. The newer no-till farming method inserts seeds directly into the unploughed soil. The unploughed soil allows the nematodes to do the job of aerating the soil instead of the plough.

Nematodes also need food in the form of decaying organic matter, which they then turn into humus. No-till farming uses previous crop residues and other organic matter as a dressing that nourishes the soil rather than the plant, which then feeds itself. Both the plants grown in humus-rich soil and animals then fed on these plants develop their own natural resistance to disease.

Darwin remarked that while the plough was one of the most ancient and valuable of man's inventions, long before it existed the land was in fact regularly ploughed, and still continues to be, by earthworms. He doubted whether there were many other organisms which played such an important part in the history of the world, and consequently in human life.

In addition to nematodes, there are also between 100 million and one billion bacteria in a cubic metre of healthy topsoil. Many of these bacteria are responsible for the decomposition and recycling of nutrients and minerals in the soil. Bacteria also interact with air and water in the soil, and with plant roots. These bacteria enable the plants to access nutrients and therefore to grow.

All of us can instinctively feel the difference between healthy living soil and inert, dead, sandy or dusty soil. The consistency and texture of soil immediately resonates with us all: healthy soil is soft, dark, moist and cloying in composition and smell, whereas unhealthy

47

soil is coarse, dry and granular, dusty-smelling and runs through your fingers.

In his quest to conquer Nature, man has failed to understand the long-term and complex nature of soil. Industrial agricultural practices are degrading and destroying this non-renewable resource. We are slow to learn from the wisdom of our ancestors, who understood how to work with and live from the soil. Modern farmers across the world are re-learning how to work with Nature, as their current farming methods are delivering diminished yields from tired soils. While modern, post-war agricultural methods using nitrogen-based fertilisers have fed the macronutrient or chemical aspects of soil, these are destroying the soil's natural microorganisms.

Since the great famine of the early 1960s, farmers in China started the intense use of nitrogen-based fertilisers. This has led to a catastrophic decline in the number of nematodes in the soil and has halved the amount of cropland once considered high quality. This destruction will necessitate the input of huge amounts of organic matter to restore the soil's structure and productivity.

Similarly, potato farmers on South Africa's West Coast have faced falling yields since early 2000, and are now reverting to applying compost rather than industrial fertilisers to restore yields. They have recognised that their soil productivity has fallen through overuse of nitrogen fertilisers that reduce the soil's natural nematode and bacteria populations.

The United Nations' Food and Agriculture Organization (FAO) has identified imbalances and deficiencies in the physical, chemical and biological conditions of soil resulting from growing single-plant crops over large areas (monoculture), compacting soil with heavy machinery and applying agrochemicals indiscriminately. Soil conservation strategies must be an integral part of sustainable agricultural development. The FAO has been promoting the benefits of no-till farming around the world through farmers' unions in individual countries. This is getting through to farmers, as the rates of adoption of no-till land management are increasing rapidly.

The transformation of our agricultural and food systems from agriculture to agri-business over the last 50 years has seen a massive re-engineering of Nature and natural processes by man. Livestock were once integrated into land management; mixed and varied crops preserved the soil and prevented erosion. Waste and by-products, whether animal or vegetable, were converted into compost for the soil. Rainwater was stored and managed and animals were left to develop their own immunity against disease.

These conditions are almost the exact opposite of modern agricultural practices, which promote vast plantings of monoculture crops like wheat. Separating animals from the plants fails to preserve the soil structure. Where animals are integrated they will eat crop residues and fertilise the soil with their manure. In much of industry, firms specialise in making one product or even a single component of that product. This sort of specialisation works well in industry, but not in farming and Nature. It is the interaction of a wide variety of plants and animals that maintains Nature's balance, in which no one species (other than man) dominates.

Specialisation works well in industry, but not in farming and Nature. It is the interaction of a wide variety of plants and animals that maintains Nature's balance.

Man has tamed four meat animals (pigs, chickens, cows and sheep), exploited four main fish types (salmon, cod, bass and tuna) and four main cereals (wheat, rice maize and soya). Where there is a natural or man-made abundance of anything, Nature registers this

49

as an imbalance and provides disease or predators to restore the balance.

The monocultures that we have developed require the continual application of pesticides or injections of antibiotics to maintain good plant and animal health. Without this constant artificial intervention our crops would go to ruin and our animals would die. Farming has followed and mimicked industrial business practices, outsourcing to specialist firms many key factors of production. There are specialist seed producers, and businesses exclusively breeding day-old chicks or producing only seed oysters for others to mature. Our food production systems have graduated from small-scale, labour-intensive and largely sustainable systems to industrial-scale, highly specialised and capital-intensive businesses.

Modern farming methods stem from man's obsession with the science of agriculture. Soil analysis and its preparation in industrial farming focuses on the three macronutrients – nitrogen (N), phosphorous (P) and potassium (K) – and as a result is often called 'NPK' farming. The less vital or secondary macro- and micronutrients as well as the biological health of soil are largely ignored. In allowing soil to be used as a commodity, to which we add man-made chemical macronutrients, we have created an agriculture industry divorced from its foundation and future – namely, healthy soil. Mined phosphate rock may peak in the next 20 years and alternatives are vital because without phosphorous fertiliser wheat and other grain yields could halve per hectare.

Industrialisation and specialisation have led man to focus on just a few grain crops, which together account for 70% of all food calories produced for human consumption. These crops were adapted from

Just a few grain crops account for 70% of all food calories produced for human consumption.

wild plants by early man, and improved by farmers through selective breeding over generations. More recently, these plants have been genetically modified by scientists to produce, for example, more grain per stalk, or to be pest- or drought-resistant.

Monoculture has increased the prevalence of animal, plant – and indeed human – disease. Instead of promoting health and immune system responses to disease, we call in the sprayers, vaccines, antibiotics and serums. This policy is failing us. Protecting crops from pests by means of pesticides and insecticides merely preserves unfit plants.

Our industrial approach, with its inherent flaws and man-made antidotes, has led to an unsustainable explosion in short-term land productivity that has enabled us to feed billions more people. It represents a transfer of the soil and Nature's accrued capital value to the current account profitability of those exploiting it.

The cost of environmental degradation or damage is not accounted for by farming or agri-businesses. In business, using a hidden balance sheet to inflate your profit and loss account is what caused Enron's collapse. In agriculture it will lead to temporary success in increasing production and profitability. All goes well as long as the soil can be made to increase yields, but soil fertility does not last forever; eventually the land is worn out or depleted. Then the accounting trick is exposed and the enterprise collapses.

This mechanisation of agriculture has freed once land-locked labour to move to the cities and fuel our urban and industrial economies. The industrialisation of our fields and high streets has happened hand-in-hand. As food retail outlets have grown in scale, so have our farms. In our own neighbourhoods, we have witnessed the disappearance of small shops and their replacement with large supermarkets and immense hypermarkets. The diversity and individuality of the small-scale has given way to larger, more uniform retail chains by a process of elimination through business efficiency and competition. As these supermarkets squeeze their supply chain (farmers) ever harder and often out of business, the agri-conglomerates, with their industrial scale and access to capital, take over and industrialise farming.

This revolution in our farming and food distribution systems has delivered many benefits. It has created an increase in production and a reduction in the price of food in the face of increased demand. Broadly speaking, food production has kept pace with the rapid increase in world population. It could conversely be argued that the advances in agricultural yields have created our global population explosion. Either way, the food system still does not work for many of our people and is showing signs of stress. As a whole, the system currently leaves just over a billion people on the edge of starvation – up from a 'low' of 788 million in 1996.

The Soil Association was founded in Sussex, United Kingdom (UK), in 1946, as even then forward thinkers, from farmers to botanists, began to understand the effects that mechanisation, plant monocultures and intensive animal rearing would have on the soil – and the potential long-term effects on agricultural production. This early awakening led to the emergence of the later organic movements. In agricultural philosophy, there is a sharp and perhaps unnecessary divide between the two camps. One side advocates the extension of existing modern agricultural methods, including the large-scale development of biotechnology and further genetic modification of monocultures. The other camp proposes a return to or rediscovery of the nature of food production, from crop rotation and organic soil nourishment to genetic diversity in crops and animals. This camp includes those like HRH the Prince of Wales, who argues that modern farming methods are fundamentally unsustainable despite their success to date.

Traditional agricultural methods recognise and use the cycles of Nature. Our modern agricultural approach is based on our understanding of mechanisation, science and technology and delivered through specialisation, automation and control. We invented mechanisation and now seek to understand ourselves and the living world in terms of our own invention. This results in an approach to agriculture based on the science of manipulation rather than the science of understanding, an economics of exploitation and a corresponding agriculture of extraction. This approach focuses on maximising short-term return with little regard for the future.

The last few years have seen the emergence of a new approach to agriculture called agro-ecology. Agro-ecology is not associated with any one particular method of farming or management practice, such as the use of natural enemies in place of insecticides, or polyculture in place of monoculture. Agro-ecologists do not unanimously oppose technology or inputs in agriculture, but instead assess how, when, and if technology can be used in conjunction with natural systems to deliver productivity, sustainability and equitable outcomes.

Using this approach, soil is not treated as an inert medium to which computer-controlled factors of production – like fertilisers – are applied. Soil is regarded as a living system in which nematodes and bacteria work to produce and maintain healthy, nutrient-rich soil. This is perhaps nothing more than using common sense in farming. In places like Madagascar, where agriculture has been relatively undisturbed by modern methods, agro-ecology is the norm. Madagascar's deforestation and massive soil erosion are a different problem. These simple ecological principles for soil management include the enhanced recycling of plant and animal matter and creating shade and windbreaks for soil protection through planting mixed woods. These woods in turn support a diverse range of animal and plant species, keeping the soil in a natural state.

53

Agriculture needs to be closely embedded in wider local ecosystems. Effective agro-ecological designs can help integrate the components of natural systems into man's requirements for agricultural production. By working with Nature rather than trying to impose our designs on natural systems, overall biological efficiency is improved, biodiversity is preserved, and the productivity and self-sustaining capacities of these agro-ecosystems are maintained.

The interconnectedness of systems in Nature continues to surprise us. In Yellowstone National Park in the American West, the wolf was hunted to local extinction some 90 years ago. Since then the number of aspen and cottonwood trees has dramatically declined, resulting in deforestation. In the absence of their natural predator, the elk population expanded and grazed down the small aspen and cottonwood saplings, preventing renewal of these once endemic trees. The absence of these trees also led to soil erosion and fewer wild birds and beaver dams.

The successful re-introduction of the wolf in mid-1995 from packs in Canada has led to increased bird and beaver populations, reduced soil erosion and better fish stocks. The aspen and cottonwood trees are flourishing again, particularly along the riverbanks.

Optimising agro-ecological processes will strengthen the natural resistance of crops against pests and disease. It will also decrease environmental toxicity by reducing the need for man-made chemicals and pesticides. Recycling our organic waste – creating effective nutrient recycling back to our gardens and fields – is starting to happen in European cities like London and Berlin. In many European cities it is now mandatory to separate organic waste from household waste; the organic waste is then composted and made available for use on our soil. This recycling initiative reduces landfill and creates a valuable product. It should become the norm worldwide.

With increasing urbanisation and mass food production systems, modern man has little interaction with Nature and often sees it as an outside force to dominate and conquer. From the urban garden to the gigantic farms and harvesting machines of the prairies, man has sought to manage and manipulate Nature for his benefit. Where his manipulation becomes a battle against Nature, humanity will eventually find himself on the losing side.

Agriculture must rapidly become part of the solution to our environmental challenges rather than a cause of environmental degradation. We need to develop an agriculture of agro-ecological systems that enhance the environment. Like Nature, farming is inherently cyclic and capable of self-renewal when properly managed. When run like a machine, as it so often is these days, farming becomes destructive, designed to suit the capitalist model of exploitation of 'free' natural capital. We ignore, at our peril, the inescapable connection between fertile soil and healthy crops, and healthy animals and healthy human beings.

We ignore, at our peril, the inescapable connection between fertile soil and healthy crops, and healthy animals and healthy human beings.

Einstein observed that the problems created by a particular way of thinking cannot be solved by the same kind of thinking. The problems created by industrial farming cannot be solved by the application of industrial solutions. In future it is likely that only agro-ecological farming operations will survive, as the cost of working against Nature will be too high. Overcoming Nature requires the application of increasingly expensive and ineffective industrial solutions from fertilisers to veterinary drugs. Those working with natural systems will end up with better quality produce and will not need these inputs in such large quantities, reducing production costs. Competition in quality and price will then eliminate those farmers who don't work in harmony with Nature.

55

There are three main factors influencing our disappearing farmland: soil erosion, soil salinisation and human settlement. As these factors drive more of our agricultural land permanently out of production, it will be hard to maintain, let alone increase, global food production levels.

Soil erosion is defined as the removal of topsoil faster than the soil forming processes can replace it. Consequently, as long as rates of soil creation and depletion are equal, there is no long-term problem. The reality is, however, that much of our global farmlands are facing huge soil erosion.

Some 25 billion tonnes of soil are being washed away each year into rivers and oceans – more than three tonnes of soil for every human on the planet.

This erosion is predominantly man-made. Destructive agricultural practices such as mechanised ploughing are responsible for just over one-third of all soil erosion. A further one-third is due to overgrazing, with the remainder due to deforestation and land clearing.

Ploughing cropland loosens the topsoil and increases the surface area exposed to the sun. It also breaks the root systems that help bind the soil together. The surface crust of soil then dries and disintegrates more easily to be carried by the wind and rains into our rivers, turning them muddy. Some 25 billion tonnes of soil are being washed away each year into rivers and oceans – more than three tonnes of soil for every human on the planet.

Recent UN (FAO) estimates put the annual loss of productive farmland worldwide at 7 million hectares, an area nearly the size of Ireland. A further 910 million hectares of once-rich land – collectively an area the size of Canada – are already moderately degraded, which means that their productivity has declined.

It is estimated that 20 percent of the world's topsoil was lost during the period 1950-1990, and that more than a third of all cropland is losing topsoil more quickly than new soil is forming. Overall, cropland represents 10% of the Earth's land surface (some 1.5 billion hectares) and grassland a further 20%.

Overgrazing on marginal rangelands reduces the plant and root cover needed to hold soils in place. Where soil erosion occurs on these often semi-arid marginal lands, they rapidly become barren or desertified and almost permanently lost to agricultural production. Nigeria is losing nearly 350,000 hectares of cropland and rangeland to desertification every year as a direct result of both farming and excessive livestock populations. Nigeria's human population expanded from 37 million in 1950 to 151 million in 2008, while its livestock population grew from 6 million to 104 million over the same period (16 million cattle and 88 million sheep and goats).

On the African continent in 1950, there were roughly 227 million people and around 300 million heads of livestock. By 2009 this had grown to one billion people and 862 million livestock. More and more animals are kept to feed our growing population.

The prize for global livestock population growth has to go to the goat. Goats can survive on land where many other animals cannot, as they will eat almost anything. Overgrazing with cattle and then sheep deteriorates the rangelands to a point where goats are the only viable livestock. Like canaries in coalmines, goats are often the harbingers of environmental devastation.

As rangelands deteriorated, the goat population in Pakistan increased six-fold between 1961 and 2009. China now has a combined sheep and goat population of 281 million. In the United States where rangelands are in better condition and still able to support larger animals such as cattle, there is a sheep-goat population of a mere 9 million animals.

57

The marginal rangelands separating the Gobi Desert from arable farmland in China is now predominantly grazed by goats. Ninety percent of China's grasslands have been degraded, while grass production is down 40% since the 1950s. Overgrazing and the establishment of 'alien' or foreign weeds – the seeds of which were brought in by the winds – have disturbed the natural ecosystems. The desert now expands into these rangelands – engulfing or desertifying some 1,400 square miles a year of once-productive land.

Degradation of these grasslands also contributes to floods, as water is no longer held in the soils by the vegetation. Water falling on the vast, rolling plateaus of western China – such as the Tibetan and Loess plateaus – runs off, carrying this soil into the great rivers, such as the Yellow River and the Yangtze. Overall erosion in China is affecting 19% of its land, and the total soil loss amounts to five billion tonnes a year.

The situation in India is no better, with nearly a quarter of its productive land slowly turning into deserts. Similar problems, even if on a smaller scale, are now affecting countries like Algeria, Chad, Kenya, Afghanistan, Iran and Iraq. Declining soil fertility and health in Lesotho, Haiti and Mongolia have resulted in reduced yields and forced these countries to become dependent on food imports and international aid. Reduced yields and increased demand can only lead to commodity and food prices rising, which affects each and every one of us.

Deforestation for firewood or to create grazing land is the third main cause of physical soil erosion. In developing countries, especially where steep, marginal land has been cleared of forests for timber and cultivation, slopes are left exposed to the effects of heavy rain.

Deforestation can result in disasters invariably described as 'natural'. The cost to human life as a result of deforestation is all too clearly illustrated by mudslides in Brazil in early 2011, which killed more than 500 people. Clearing of trees along the Indus Valley has led to a build-up of silt in the river system, which then could not cope with the unusually heavy monsoon rains of July 2010. More than 2,000 Pakistanis lost their lives and millions more were displaced as 20% of the country's land was flooded.

All these types of environmental degradation end in topsoil being carried away by water. This muddy water affects not only aquatic life and other ecosystems, but also man's use of the rivers and their waters.

The cost to human life as a result of deforestation is all too clearly illustrated by mudslides in Brazil in early 2011, which killed more than 500 people.

The two largest reservoirs in Pakistan lose around 1% of their storage capacity every year as they fill up with silt as a direct result of water-borne topsoil. Over time as these reservoirs silt up, their storage capacity will reduce and therefore so will the water available for irrigation and drinking.

The largest annual transfer of soil – amounting to 1.6 billion tonnes – is delivered by the Huang River into the East China Sea. Sediment accumulating in rivers has cut navigation channels by 50% and therefore reduced the size of boats that can operate on them.

It is not only water that erodes unprotected or degraded soil from our land. Wind erosion also occurs when the soil has little or no vegetation to hold it in place. Unprotected soil can be blown off by storms at a rate of up to 150 tonnes an hour from each hectare of land. Dust and sand storms are becoming increasingly prevalent the world over as marginal lands are stripped of their remaining vegetation.

The first major dust storm or 'Dust Bowl' in modern history was in the mid-western United States between 1930 and 1936. It caused major

59

damage to America's agricultural systems. Deep ploughing of the Great Plains displaced its deep-rooted grasses that previously secured the soil and trapped moisture – even during droughts. This deep ploughing was made possible by early mechanisation and fed by a desire to grow crops rather than maintain the indigenous grasslands for animal grazing. The newly turned soil, combined with reduced rainfall, turned the fields to dust that blew away in huge, rolling clouds. This degradation of the land caused a mass migration of people from rural areas to the cities and extraordinary economic hardship during this transition.

Today 21st-century dust bowls are in the making. A town in north-west Texas, ironically named 'Happy', is the unfortunate harbinger of bad news. This farming community relies on water from the aquifer under its land to water its crops. Local officials announced in March 2010 that the aquifer was dry. The immense Ogallala aquifer in fact slopes, and is deep underground at one extremity and nearer the surface just under Happy. The water from this aquifer, if spread across the US, would cover all 50 states nearly 50 centimeters deep. While the rest of that region will be able to continue farming for some years to come, residents of Happy are concerned that their land will dry up and echo the desiccation across the Great Plains in the thirties. The people of Happy have understood that to farm using an unsustainable source of water is just that – unsustainable.

Annual dust storms are now a regular occurrence in eastern China as the remaining vegetation on marginal rangelands is eaten and the Gobi Desert expands. A particularly severe dust storm in March 2010, affecting an estimated 250 million people, blew straight across the Chinese mainland and into South Korea. The choking dust clouds blocked out sunlight and caused widespread breathing difficulties for those in its path. A number of dust storms originating in China have been tracked as far as the east coast of the United States.

Dust bowls can form either as a result of overgrazing, as in China today, or from over-ploughing, as in the US in the 1930s. During the 1960s the then-Soviet Union unwittingly created a dust bowl of its own. In an attempt to make a grain belt centred on the Kazakhstan region, the former USSR ploughed up grasslands and diverted rivers to irrigate the grain. As the rivers ran dry, the crops failed and a dust bowl ensued. Drought and overgrazing are already laying the foundation for dust bowls in the Sahel belt across North Africa – a fragile scrubland that separates the Sahara desert from the more fertile lands of the equatorial belt to the south.

Conservation and restoration projects are already underway in parts of India and China. We have to support and encourage these initiatives. In India, 6 trillion tonnes of soil are lost annually from the 80 million hectares under cultivation. Unprotected land may lose between 120 and 300 tonnes of soil per hectare in a single year.

The Loess Plateau in north-central China is home to over 50 million people. It takes its name from the dry, dusty soil created by years of overgrazing and unsustainable farming. Over a 10-year period, from 1994 to 2005, the area was extensively rehabilitated. This process began with the extensive planting of trees, especially on hilltops. Planting trees prevents water erosion and flooding from run-off, allowing the soil to retain moisture while the growing trees also act as a windbreak. Gradually terraces were built and the soil structure was restored and enriched with organic matter. Water was carefully conserved and food grown for local communities, increasing local employment. This exemplifies the agro-ecological approach – where the whole landscape is restored and once again made productive. Every such project enhances the food security and wealth of local communities.

The soil left on our land is also being taken out of use for food production at an alarming rate. There are four main causes: excessive mineral build-up or salinisation in the soil; wasteful production of biofuels; man's increasing use of land to accommodate a rapidly expanding global population; and climate change.

61

Irrigation with deep groundwater rich in minerals can lead to salinisation of the soil – an ongoing problem for some 6,000 years. There are two main causes of salinisation. First, where land is cleared of trees and shrubs that are resistant to saline water, groundwater levels rise and bring saline water to the root table, affecting those crops not adapted to salt. Where no groundcover is planted and when fields are fallow, this effect is exacerbated as more water sinks into the ground, which raises the saline water table.

Secondly, salinisation can be caused by repeated application of mineral-rich (salinated) water drawn from deep underground onto topsoil where salt builds up. This is particularly prevalent in drier areas such as the grain belts of China and the US, or in areas of India where they cannot effectively store their rainfall for later use and rely on underground water sources. At least 20% of all irrigated land is already salt-affected. As we engineer our food crops to require less irrigation, we also need to engineer salt-tolerant varieties.

In Australia there have been multiple environmental impacts which, if we allow current trends to continue, offer a preview of what we are up against. Australian soils already have low-nutrient and high-salt levels, which translate into poor growth rate and low productivity.

High mineral salt concentrations make it harder for the roots of plants to absorb water, as well as having a more general toxic effect on certain crops. Drip irrigation poses less of a problem, as less water is used on the soil. Broadcast irrigation systems, however, using overhead sprinklers or other means, saturate the ground with more water than can be absorbed by plants' roots. Minerals seep into the soil, increasing the rate of salinisation.

This form of soil degradation already affects nearly 10% of cleared agricultural ground in Australia and is forecast to rise to 25% by 2030. Almost eight million hectares of irrigated land in India – 20% of its land – are now affected by salinisation; the comparable percentage in China is already 10%.

The second factor taking land out of food production is its alternative use for biofuel production. The principal commercial biofuels are ethanol, derived from sugar cane, and agri-diesel, derived from palm oil. They were originally touted as an ecologically sound means of combating climate change through their substitution for fossil fuels. The subsidies available to farmers to grow these biofuels made them very attractive. Land previously used to grow crops for the human food chain was diverted to grow the more profitable biofuel crops. In the US an understandable political imperative is to reduce dependence on foreign oil supply.

The US spends more than $170 billion a year on importing oil, mostly from unfriendly nation states whom they are enriching.

High mineral salt concentrations make it harder for the roots of plants to absorb water, as well as having a more general toxic effect on certain crops.

Current ethanol production in Brazil takes up 6 million hectares of land, but the target is 30 million hectares producing 100 trillion litres of ethanol per year. Malaysia and Indonesia are the primary producers of palm oil, with 6 million hectares already under cultivation between them. In Indonesia alone a further 18 million hectares of forest are being cleared for palm oil production, with yet a further 20 million hectares under threat. All this adds to the destructive effect on a country that has already lost 72% of its ancient forests.

In 2008 some 18% of grain production in the US was devoted to biofuels. This could otherwise have fed 250 million people with their average grain requirements. In 2009 more than a quarter of the US grain production was used in biofuels.

This substitution of food crops for fuel crops was a major factor in the rise of commodity and food prices in 2007-2008. The subsidies for biofuels have escalated the pace of the destruction of woodlands and forests. At that time decisions were being made on the basis of short-term profits, political imperatives and subsidies rather than long-term sustainability: the food crisis meets the energy crisis.

The real issue here is not creating an alternative, but reducing the chronic American addiction to cheap fuel. If the true cost, including the environmental damage of the fuel, was included in the retail fuel price, America would suffer a material price shock. Like Europeans who have far higher fuel prices, they would have to trade in their gas guzzlers for fuel-efficient cars.

The average American household's electricity bill is less than one-third of that in Europe. Electricity pricing does not reinforce the energy-saving culture that it does in Europe. If Americans were to switch to low-energy lighting, the US could close down several coal-powered power stations, save money and reduce its carbon emissions.

From the early '90s US car manufacturers like Ford produced fuel-efficient engines and cars all over the world, yet at home they continued to sell the standard large-engine gas guzzlers, convinced that American consumers preferred them. They misread their home market, as many of their consumers switched to the then more fuel-efficient Japanese motorcars, and they are now playing catch-up.

The third factor taking farmland out of production is man himself. Most cities have expanded from early settlements often located in fertile areas near rivers and estuaries. With industrialisation, urbanisation and rising populations comes more demand for infrastructure, factories and housing. Increasing wealth requires more roads for cars, more shopping centres and car parks and more leisure facilities such as tennis courts. More than 40 new golf courses were planned for 2010 in China's Gaungdong province alone.

This demand for land takes prime cropland out of production and leads to declining production levels. If trends from countries that have undergone rapid industrialisation are anything to go by, then China's grain land area will shrink by around 50% over 40 years, or at a rate of about 1.2% a year. Japan used to be self-sufficient in grain, but as it has grown wealthier and used up its farmland, it now has to import 70% of its requirement.

Already millions of workers in China have migrated from the country to towns, and they all need housing. Rising divorce rates and the one-child policy are increasing the number of households in China. Increasing affluence also means that people will want more space.

For every 100 million workers, around one million factories will need to be built, each of which takes up space and requires its own access roads and parking. Then there is a corresponding expansion of the road infrastructure: 1.15 million cars were sold in China in 1990, rising to 15.5 million in 2010 alone, and the 2011 figure is expected to top 20 million. In addition, appropriation of land for mining, forestry and even aquaculture, as well as rubbish dump sites, has contributed to polluting the soil and reducing and damaging cropland.

The fourth factor that may substantially reduce our productive farmland is climate change. We have experienced ice-free periods in history, but sea levels then were some 70 metres higher. As we enter another period of climate change, one of the major consequences will be rising sea levels.

Most productive farmland is on low-lying ground and around estuaries, rich in topsoil washed down from higher ground. As sea levels rise the resulting flooding will therefore have a disproportionate effect on farmland and on food-producing soils. A few degrees' rise in global temperature will see both polar and Greenland ice melt – releasing water into the seas and raising sea levels by several metres. A rise of a metre or less would devastate the rice-growing river delta areas of Asia, on which much of the population depends for its staple food. Such a small rise seems almost certain in our lifetime, given the far larger predictions of most climate scientists. Since most humans live in low, coastal areas, existing inland farmland will be further affected as people move to higher ground.

Our disappearing farmland and climate change are creating uncertainty around global food supply. Food insecurity is driven by rising populations unable to be sustained on the land and water resources within a country's borders. Wealthy but food-poor countries concerned about their existing and future food security are increasingly buying or leasing land offshore to grow crops.

Saudi Arabia, for example, was able to grow up to three million tonnes of grain per year during the last 20 years, but they have now all but exhausted the underground aquifer that provided water to irrigate their crops. Crop yields declined by two-thirds between 2007 and 2010, and it is estimated that the last harvest of grain will take place in 2012. Without agricultural investment abroad, Saudi Arabia would be particularly vulnerable to market supply. Saudi Arabia may be oil-rich but it is water and food-poor. Despite its large landmass, it cannot sustain its 28 million people.

Generally, the investor country acquiring land in another country puts the unused land into production by investing heavily in infrastructure to service the project. Agreements typically leave some of the produce in the country albeit at market prices. It is not necessarily about price but rather security of physical supply for the investing country.

This approach involves using not just the host country's land but also its water – in a sense it is a financial land and water grab that in the past may have been achieved by war. Where the country also has huge labour resources such as China, it also exports its labour to work the farms, providing few – if any – benefits for the host country. It is estimated that some one million Chinese labourers are working on farms in Africa; in Zambia, for instance, Chinese-operated farms produce a quarter of the eggs sold in Lusaka.

Offshore investment in agricultural production of this nature helps to establish and ensure a semi-reliable physical supply of agricultural produce. The reliability of these schemes must be qualified since – as we have seen in India, Russia, Chile and other countries – when local harvests fail, the host country bans produce exports. Between 2006 and 2009, 15 to 20 million hectares were acquired in Africa by foreign sovereign states for production of food staples such as wheat, maize and rice for export to their home territories.

The world's largest offshore land investor is China, with 2.8 million hectares in the Congo alone. Controversially, China's holding in the Congo is devoted to the production of palm oil for biofuel, which is energy- rather than food-related. This highlights China's unease about its growing dependence on foreign oil with its rapidly expanding car fleet. China's total global holdings are hard to estimate as many of these deals are deliberately kept out of the public eye.

In the offshore land investment rankings, China dwarfs other investors. South Korea has nearly 800,000 hectares; United Arab Emirates around 780,000 hectares; and Saudi Arabia and Qatar, around 450,000 hectares each. This foreign land investment in Africa equates with France's total agricultural land.

Sudan has said that it will reserve up to 20% of its agricultural land for the Gulf States, even though

The world's largest offshore land investor is China, with 2.8 million hectares in the Congo alone. In Kazakhstan, China's proposal to lease one million hectares to grow soya for animal feed and other grain crops led to mass protest by affected locals.

some of its own population is starving and the country already receives international food aid. One can only wonder what deals were negotiated to facilitate such a human catastrophe.

For the host country, an offshore investment can represent a welcome boost to developing its agricultural infrastructure. In some cases local opposition has prevented prospective investment, as in Madagascar where resistance led to the overthrow of President Marc Ravalomanana in March 2009. In Kazakhstan, China's proposal to lease one million hectares to grow soya for animal feed and other grain crops led to mass protest by affected locals in March 2011 – and the proposal was dropped.

China has 22% of the world population but only 7% of global arable land. This fact alone makes China vulnerable. With its shrinking land base and water shortages this risk is increased. A huge emerging middle-class now able to afford meat is fuelling the demand for cereals as animal feed and compounding the problem.

Most of these offshore investor land deals have been brokered by the sovereign wealth funds of these states. Agricultural `offshoring' is becoming a vital political priority and the practice will continue to expand as wealthy countries seek to ensure their food security.

Food is not as cheap as it may seem in the shops; in reality you pay in many ways – mostly indirectly – for the food you purchase. You pay once at the supermarket checkout and again through income taxes which provide subsidies for farmers, and pay for cleaning up the direct environmental as well as health side-effects. The long-term environmental costs are still unaccounted for at this stage – and therefore remain hidden. British farmers spend £500 million a year on pesticides, but it costs consumers indirectly a further £120 million, recovered through the cost of water, to clean the pesticide residues out of drinking water. The true cost of food

British farmers spend £500 million a year on pesticides, and it costs a further £120 million to clean the residues out of drinking water.

is not internalised in the price you pay, but is shifted elsewhere.

Few people are aware of the costs of damage caused by pesticides, microorganisms and other disease agents. Conservative estimates put the annual costs in Britain alone at well over £1 billion for damage to the atmosphere, water, biodiversity, landscapes, soils and – last but not least – human health.

Recent academic research has shown a significant loss of minerals and trace elements in fruit and vegetables over the last 50 years as soil health has declined. The old adage of an apple a day no longer applies. You now need to eat three apples in order to provide your daily-recommended intake of minerals such as copper or zinc.

People are now eating more prepared foods than ever before. These foods are devoid of micronutrients and packed with chemical additives such as colourings, flavourings and preservatives. These dietary and food quality changes have contributed significantly to rising levels of diet-induced ill health. Where people are eating too much of the wrong food, they do not get an adequate supply of basic nutrients – leading to what is technically known as 'overconsumptive undernutrition'. Our current farming and food system continues to fuel this trend.

With land – even more so than with water – we face issues of overexploitation of a finite resource. We have misunderstood the nature of soil as we have industrialised and grown distant from it. Unlike water and desalinisation, there is no back-up for our soil. There are hydroponic solutions that would enable life to continue but would not save our lands.

69

Our challenge is that our land is already under pressure at the same time as our population is increasing along with its demand for food, while at the same time climate change is expected to have an adverse effect on grain yields. The current agricultural food system as a whole cannot keep pace and is unsustainable. Our 'use and abuse' of food, with more than one billion people overweight alongside one billion on the verge of starvation, is obscene.

To feed our growing population we have little choice but to develop agro-ecological initiatives to restore our croplands; reforest our hills and river systems; stop wasting the produce of our land; and recycle the nutrients we throw away as landfill back into our soil.

CHAPTER THREE – SEAS

Fish came before man, yet their histories have been interwoven for thousands of years. The limitless abundance of fish in our rivers, lakes and oceans once seemed assured, yet today the destruction of our fresh water and sea fish stocks is imminent – a direct result of our greed, stupidity and technical brilliance.

A close look around your local supermarket will tell you that our seas are in danger. Baby hake or sole petite fillets in the frozen section are there not because they are tastier or easier to catch, but simply because we have eaten their parents. The fishmonger's ice slab in the same supermarket probably displays only a few full-size fish. Most of these will be farmed fish like salmon and trout or crustaceans like shrimps and prawns. These farmed fish and crustaceans have been fed on 'fishmeal', other small sea fish like anchovies and sand eels that are processed and ground into pellets. Twenty years ago a sole ordered in a restaurant filled your plate; now you often get two smaller ones in a serving. You don't need to be a farmer to understand that if you are eating your breeding stock, you are in deep trouble.

The Canadian government pandered to its fishermen and allowed clearly unsustainable fishing to continue in the 1980s and early 1990s. Fish catches and, most importantly, the size of fish caught were falling rapidly. With much of the mature breeding fish caught and eaten, stocks rapidly collapsed. With almost no fish left, 80,000 Canadians in the fishing industry lost their jobs, and the fisheries of the Grand Banks closed in 1992 after 500 years of fishing. Today, nearly 20 years later, they are still closed and the world has lost a unique and, if managed sustainably, renewable natural resource.

Israel's Sea of Galilee has been a spiritual home for fishermen since the time of Christ, and for many thousands of years it sustained the local population. Fishing was banned on Galilee in April 2010 because there are almost no breeding-size fish left. The main catch was the St Peter's

73

fish – so called after a passage in the Bible in which Peter catches a fish with a coin in its mouth. These fish were once amazingly abundant. Before 1995, 295 tonnes of St Peter's fish were caught annually. Then stocks collapsed and in 2009 the catch was only eight tonnes.

On a tour of the Western Cape region in 2009, South African President Jacob Zuma was accosted by Struisbaai fishermen who complained that they could no

Fishing was banned on the Sea of Galilee in April 2010 as there are almost no fish left

longer make a living wage from the seas, as there were not enough fish. President Zuma responded that if they want to catch more fish they should stop fishing for a year. Coming from a farming community, the President evidently understands the basic laws of Nature, unlike many other world leaders.

As early hunter-gatherers sought protein they became the first fishermen and exploited the then abundant river fish. European rivers in the 13th century were crowded with fish. Salmon was so abundant that it was a fish for the poor, who complained at being fed nothing else. As Europe's humanity polluted its rivers, freshwater fishermen moved to the seas to catch the next most freely available source of protein.

Later mariners caught and salted cod, which then allowed man to explore the oceans while carrying his food. Many early mariners' maps show areas recorded as having plentiful supplies of fish, and are annotated with legends like 'much crowded with variety of seafood', or 'cod and ling of great size'. The talk in the 17th and 18th centuries was of abundance, as if the seas could never run out of fish.

The earliest fishermen to explore the New World were the Vikings, but it was not until the late 15th and early 16th centuries that commercial exploitation really began. The rivers of the New World ran clear – unlike those of medieval Europe which by then were already blocked with weirs and clogged with silt from farming and deforestation. The rivers of Newfoundland teemed with fish, described as almost containing more fish than water. The size of these wild, unexploited fish was also immense. Early explorers recorded sturgeon the size of a great white shark, weighing more than a fully-grown cow.

Subsistence estuary and near-shore marine fishing began centuries ago in small boats, providing food for the local community. One of the first large-scale marine fishing ventures was the launch of the herring industry in the 1700s, which employed as many as 20,000 people in Scotland alone. In Wick, in the north of Scotland, a record fleet of 1,122 boats and 3,800 fishermen used the harbour in the summer of 1862. Staggeringly, 3,500 fisherwomen gutted 50 million herring brought in by these boats in just two days, at the rate of between 60 and 70 a minute!

Small-scale fishing had become industrialised and the battle was on to maximise profit and harvest as much 'free' fish as possible to feed Europe's growing population, with little thought to the sustainability of the seas. So convinced were fishermen of the seas' infinite abundance that they hardly noticed their catches decline. Had any decline been noticed it would have simply been considered seasonal.

The two World Wars took the pressure off North Sea fish stocks, as fishing was too hazardous, enabling fish numbers to recover. The aftermath of the First World War saw a glut of herring as stocks were high and the British government discouraged exports to Russia. Previously, this trade amounted to one million barrels of herring a year. Oversupply led to a collapse of prices and catches were often dumped back into the sea. By 1939, however, the United Kingdom's herring stocks were once again so depleted that fishing became uneconomical, and fishermen were laid off in substantial numbers.

75

The greatest losses in fish stocks were sustained following the industrial intensification of fishing after the Second World War. Since then worldwide breeding stocks of species such as cod, haddock and halibut have fallen by up to 90%. It is ironic that fishermen now concentrate on fish like herring that were used only as bait in the days of plentiful cod and halibut.

The first battles over declining fish stocks came with the British and Icelandic cod wars of the 1970s. Skirmishes over access to fishing grounds between the two nations had occurred sporadically since the 1950s. At the time fishermen viewed the right to plunder and harvest the seas at will as a national right. Little thought was given to the reason for the skirmishes: the overfished and decreasing cod stocks. The Icelandic government and their fishermen realised this. Iceland declared a 4, then 12 then 50 and in 1975 a 200 nautical mile (NM) Exclusive Economic Zone (EEZ) around their islands (the global 200 NM limit was recognised by the UN only in 1982). This EEZ was set up in an effort to protect Icelandic fish stocks and, more importantly, their breeding grounds from the rapacious international trawling operations. It was this series of actions that led to a number of skirmishes between the fishermen and navies of the two countries. This included the cutting of trawlers' nets by the Icelandic navy and tugs, trawlers and frigates of both nations ramming each other in what were named the Icelandic Cod Wars.

Ports and fisheries around Europe are already in decline. In Scotland, the historic Aberdeen Fish Market has seen falling fish catches. The tonnage of white fish landed in Aberdeen between 2002 and 2006 fell 59%. The catch landed in the first quarter of 2007 was 71% lower than that in the same period in 2006 as local fish stocks collapsed. The Aberdeen Fish Market was no longer viable and closed in 2010. Other ports further south – like Grimsby, Hull and Fleetwood – are shadows of their formerly prosperous selves. In the 19th century, boats could be found up to 10 abreast in Grimsby harbour, the quay bustled with activity and fishing boats were still followed by pods of porpoises and dolphins. Some of the fish, like cod and halibut, were so large that they could be sold individually. In the 1960s Grimsby still supported large processing plants like the Ross Group. Much of the fishing activity of these ports has, however, now ceased.

Humans since early man have always consumed fish. Throughout early Christian Europe, fish was mandated as part of its devotees' diets. Catholic dietary laws restricted the consumption of red meat not only on Fridays, but also on other fast days, which at that time made up almost half the calendar year. In much of the world marine-caught fish has become part of the national culture – for example, pickled herring in the Netherlands and fish and chips in Britain.

Four fish have defined much of recent human history: salmon, tuna, bass and cod. Cod is the most significant, as it has changed human history more than any other fish. In 1497, the Italian explorer John Cabot sailed across the Atlantic Ocean to what he called 'New Founde Lande'. He reported that the cod were so numerous in the water off the coast that they sometimes halted the progress of his ship, and that they could be caught simply by dropping a basket into the water and hauling in the catch.

Cod were once so plentiful off the coast of Newfoundland that they impeded the passage of ships.

The fact that cod store oil in their liver and not in their flesh makes them a better fish to preserve. This prompted their industrial exploitation and eventual demise. The news about plentiful cod spread fast, and by 1517 around 50 ships a year were bringing back preserved cod from Western Canada. By 1550, as boats became progressively more seaworthy, more than 400 ships a season were crossing the Atlantic to bring cod back from the Grand Banks fishing grounds. The British had joined this fishing bonanza along the Newfoundland coast by about 1600, some 20 years before the *Mayflower* sailed from

Plymouth with the Pilgrim Fathers to found what is now modern-day America.

Nearer to home in the 19th century, herring were so abundant that contemporary reports claimed that when the migratory fish arrived in shoals five or six miles long and three or four miles wide off Britain's coasts, they altered the very appearance of the seas. It is understandable that fishermen then thought that the supply of fish was inexhaustible.

Natural predators follow the migratory herring shoals in British waters, as they do the sardine runs off South Africa's east coast. These predators include pods of whales, sharks, dolphins and giant tuna. Fishermen followed the movements of these predators to locate the herring, and even had to fight them off as they tried to eat the fish caught in their nets. When the herring and sardines were plentiful they were also preyed upon from above by thousands of diving seabirds, again indicating the location of the shoals. Herring migrate into shallow coastal waters to mate and lay their eggs; they and their millions of eggs are food for the shoals of cod and haddock. Essentially, fish stocks are delicately balanced marine ecosystems.

There is a long history of fishermen complaining that their competitors – both local and international – are overfishing and depleting stocks. From the early use of hook and line from rowing boats, sail ships were then used in the middle ages to drag nets or 'trawl' through the water or latterly along the seabed. Many medieval fishermen filed legal complaints to try to prevent or at least restrict this practice. History suggests that even then, commercial sea fishing was adversely affecting herring and cod populations.

Another commonly used technique was a longline of then up to several hundred metres set with many baited hooks. By the 1860s,

British driftnet herring fishermen were claiming that these longliners were fishing unsustainably by catching too many fish. They were finding that there were not enough herring in their own grounds, and that they had to go further out to sea to find new fishing areas. This prompted the British government to establish the Thomas Huxley Commission in 1862 to look into the issue.

The Commission dismissed the concerns of the herring fishermen as "unscientific," not because they had accurately gauged the annual catch in relation to the overall stock, but because the commissioners and others believed that the seas were inexhaustible and that Nature was sufficiently resilient to adapt to any human impact on the environment. It was believed that the number of sea fish caught by fishermen was insignificant in relation to the stocks and the greater burden of natural predation.

By the end of the 19th century a further British Parliamentary enquiry overturned the previous government's view that fish stocks were inexhaustible, but by then the decline in British fisheries had already begun and thereafter continued at an alarming rate. As fishing methods industrialised, fish stocks were quickly affected – between 1890 and 1900 trawler catches fell by 50%.

The new steam-powered trawling boats introduced by British fishing fleets in the 19th century heralded the arrival of the industrial fishing era. These boats were capable of trawling the 260,000 square kilometres of the North Sea twice a year. An 1883 map of the North Sea bed indicates an area the size of Wales as 'oysters', a collection of interlinked reefs composed of oysters and other invertebrates. Bottom trawling rapidly transformed this rich marine habitat into a vast expanse of gravel, sand and mud – a watery desert. Like the Grand Banks, this was a sustainable marine resource that mans greed has completely destroyed. The last living oyster was caught in this area in the 1970s.

79

The near-shore fishermen of Nigeria have been complaining since the 1980s that their fish have disappeared and they can no longer make a living because of unregulated offshore fishing by international fleets. The European Union (EU), amongst others, has purchased rights for their fishermen and their trawlers to catch fish off the West African coast.

This industrial and sophisticated trawling has dramatically reduced the number of fish available to the millions of Nigerians who depend on fishing for a living. These fishermen provide the nation with 75% of their fish – a staple diet and source of protein for the country. Both the marine fishermen and the inland fishermen are under threat. Overfishing has caused economic hardship for the Kainji dam fishermen of western Nigeria. The fishermen of lake Chad in northern Nigeria face a different issue. One third of the waters of lake Chad lay inside Nigeria's national borders as recently as 1930. The receding waters of this lake, once Africa's largest freshwater lake, are now no longer inside the country's borders as its surface area shrank by 95% between 1963 and 1996. The unsustainable use of the lake's waters for agriculture is now being compounded as the Nigerian fishermen have now turned to farming what were once the lake bottom and their fishing grounds.

Fishing sustains the local economy along many coastlines of the world. It is estimated that up to 800 million people globally live directly from the coastal seas. The majority of these are subsistence fishermen who fish to feed themselves and directly sustain their families. Fishing boats are often owned jointly by a number of families working in partnership. Catches provide not only a livelihood for fishermen, but also for those involved in ancillary industries such as boat building and fish processing. Any fluctuation in the profitability of fishing therefore ripples out and impacts on the local community.

If fishermen are practical experts in marine matters, then scientists can claim to be theoretical experts by assessing the impact of fishing practices on overall estimated fish stocks. Conflict often arises between fishermen and scientists when the latter recommend restrictions on catches, upon which the fishermen's livelihoods depend.

A further issue is that much of the scientific research upon which governments base their decisions is funded by the fishing industry itself. Often this research recommends fishing quotas that preserve the status quo. The fishing industry lobby then uses this 'evidence' and its PR machine to minimise the impact of individuals raising concerns about overfishing.

Politicians in fishing constituencies from Canada to the United Kingdom depend on the votes of fishermen to get elected. Fishermen rather than fish have the vote. Politicians often find themselves being squeezed between votes and jobs or continued overfishing. The line of least resistance for politicians is invariably to recommend higher levels of catch than are sustainable, hence potentially damaging the long-term interests of the community, although not the short-term interests of their constituents.

Often it is the lone, passionate individuals that can see through the noise of vested business interests. Had we listened to the scientists who proffered evidence that whale catches were sustainable rather than to those passionate individuals desperate to save our whales, we might well have no whales left today. Had we listened to those advocating the establishment of national marine reserves decades ago, we would have many more fish in our seas today.

Should we listen to those individuals who are passionate about the environment or the government and their scientific advisors? Remember: a lone amateur built the Ark, and a large group of professionals built the *Titanic*.

81

Advances in fishing equipment and technology have vastly increased the efficiency of fishing fleets and the size of their catches. This has accelerated the depletion of marine fish stocks. Moreover, as boats become more expensive to buy, the skippers have to land more fish in order to pay the huge loans against these craft, which makes the impact of any downturn all the more drastic. The boats and equipment of the world fishing industry were estimated to be worth US$376 billion in 2010, with one-third of decked fishing boats now being Chinese-owned. It is not only the capital investment but also the running costs that have increased. In 1999 it took one litre of diesel to catch a kilo of fish: in 2010 it took almost two litres of diesel to catch the same kilo of fish, as the boats had to sail further and trawl deeper to fill their nets.

Individual countries now have national fishing exclusion zones around their coasts for up to 200 nautical miles. These are patrolled by wealthier nations but often unregulated in poorer regions. Most of the world's oceans are open seas, indivisible and unregulated. Free for all to use, this vital resource must be exploited sustainably, not fished to the point of decline – and likely ultimate destruction.

The open seas have facilitated maritime trade but also allowed unfettered access to their fish stocks. The oceans have worked sustainably to provide fish for centuries, while the demand for fish and the numbers of fishermen could be supported sustainably by the natural bounty of the sea. The freedom of the seas has now, however, brought many species to the brink of extinction. An unrestricted number of fishermen, unconstrained by limits on their catch, are able to extract profit from the seas. They add to their individual profit and loss accounts without any regard for the world's balance sheet of marine life. As long as the fisherman makes a

As long as the economics work, greed will prevail and fishermen will trawl for the last fish in the seas.

profit, greed will prevail and fishermen will trawl for the last fish in the seas. When the last fisherman catches the last fish, it is no longer his problem but all of ours.

Fishermen have little incentive to practice conservation, reasoning that if they themselves do not catch the available fish, someone else will. Take, for example, a small and contained fishing system like the Sea of Galilee, shared by several fishing communities. Faced with falling catches, fishing communities sharing the common resource will fish harder to maintain incomes. They presume that if they do not take the remaining fish, the other fishing communities will. While they may well understand that this will lead to catastrophe for all of the communities, that is tomorrow's problem! The same is true of the seas. Fortunately, the fish of the Sea of Galilee will probably be saved by state intervention.

This leaves us globally locked into an unsustainable, profit-driven system heading towards disaster. Ignoring the reality of our overfishing is as sensible as ignoring the fuel gauge on your car on a long journey. To compound this madness, governments globally subsidise the fishing industry to the tune of US$17.6 billion a year. These subsidies hide the real cost of fish to the consumer and contribute to an excess capacity of boats, equipment and fishermen – and hence to the depletion of fish stocks.

International trawling for cod on the Grand Banks provided an amazing harvest, but eventually the fishing intensity began to outpace the ability of its stocks of cod fish stock to replace itself. The stock of cod actually fell by 90% between the early 1960s and the late 1980s. Cod typically start breeding at between four and six years old and can live up to 20 years of age. Intensive fishing has removed many of these bigger fish, with the result that breeding slowed down and dwindling numbers of young cod joined the breeding stock.

A large, healthy and genetically varied spawning stock is essential to the survival of any species. Once fish stocks of a species dip below this minimum diversity level, scientists believe that stocks may never recover because their entire ecosystem has effectively been broken. In previously cod-rich areas, the ecosystem shift has meant that the fishing effort is now directed to high-value and now prolific shellfish, crab and shrimp, which were once eaten by the cod. The somewhat ironic result is that this industry is making more profit now than the cod fishery did in the 1980s.

A similar overfishing of cod occurred in the North Sea, but not to the point of collapse of the species. Cod stock in the North Sea may once have been as high as seven million tonnes, but by the 1970s and the onset of the cod wars this had been reduced to 250,000 tonnes. In 2006 continued overfishing depleted the stock further to a low of 35,700 tonnes, prompting further reductions in quotas. In 2010 stocks had recovered by more than 50% since this low point, but this is hardly cause for celebration. Stocks of cod landed by English and Welsh boats have declined by 86% in the past 100 years. The Marine Stewardship Council (MSC) was set up to provide advice to consumers on the sustainability of fish supplies through monitoring the fisheries and promoting sustainable fishing. The MSC is maintaining its advice to consumers not to eat North Sea cod.

B ig ships and their fishing technology have driven a lot of the world's fishing over capacity. Small inshore boats, however, still comprise a large proportion of the total world fishing fleet. The number of fishing vessels powered by engines was estimated to be just over two million in 2006, of which almost 70% were concentrated in Asia.

Steam-powered drifters took over from sail boats in Britain in the late 19th century, followed by larger motorised boats capable of remaining longer at sea. Until then, both wind and tide had limited the effectiveness of sailing trawlers, so boats could work only close inshore. The power of steam transformed the fishing capacity by enabling boats to work in almost any weather, with or against the wind and tide.

The first factory trawlers were launched in Europe and the United States in the 1950s, which led to a rapid increase in total world catch. They could catch and process hundreds of tonnes of fish a day without having to return to port. This capacity also enabled them to travel to other waters when their own domestic fishing grounds were depleted.

In the past fishermen were led to abundant fishing grounds by birds and predators. Now they use sonar technology developed from radar during the Second World War. This technology enabled fleets of factory trawlers to locate and track large schools of fish and trap them en masse before moving on to the next target area. This was the beginning of industrial fishing, helping to drive up the total quantity of catch and leading ultimately to depletion of stocks.

The advent of plastics technology and powerful trawlers has changed the industry dramatically. Irrespective of the level of the sea being fished – deep or surface – the principle of an immense net being dragged through the seas is the same. This trawling process has been developed into the 'purse seine' net, the principal method used today. The purse seine net, up to 3,000 metres long, is spread by a pair of boats below a shoal of fish – like tuna – which is then hoisted to the surface as the 'strings' of the net are pulled together like a purse. This indiscriminately traps fish of all sizes and maturity in the target species as well as a large amount of other fish.

Globally, there are more than 38,000 fishing vessels in excess of 100 tonnes. The largest freezing trawler is the now Dutch-owned *Annelies Ilena,* which cost £50 million to build and is 145 metres long. Operating off the coast of Brittany, she is capable of catching,

85

processing and freezing up to 350 tonnes of fish a day and holding 7,000 tonnes of graded and frozen fish on board.

National fishing grounds have expanded in size and these fishing rights have become saleable. The UN gave coastal nations the rights to develop fisheries within a 200 nautical mile exclusive economic zone (EEZ). If these countries did not have developed fishing industries they could grant harvesting rights to other countries. Since the 1970s, the EU has both subsidised European fishing boats and signed access agreements with West African countries for them to fish within their respective National fishing zones. In 1996 alone, the EU paid US$229 million for access agreements with Africa. This is more than 40% of the budget that was earmarked for restructuring its oversized fleet – not on acquiring new fishing grounds.

We now have too many fishermen, too many boats and too many hooks and nets taking too many the fish out of the sea.

The rent received by these African countries often averages less than 10% of the value of the catch. This essentially means that they are exporting a valuable natural food resource, at low cost, from African countries to richer EU nations. A 2002 EU report revealed that the Senegalese fish biomass had declined 75% in 15 years. In that same year, however, the EU bought extensive fishing access rights for its member states in Africa. It purchased four years of fishing access for tuna and bottom-dwelling fish like sole off the Senegalese coast, for just US$4 million per year.

Then in 2006, the EU bought access for 43 giant factory-fishing vessels to exploit Mauritania's coastline for £24.3 million per year. The knock-on effect is that these deals have forced almost 400,000 West African fishermen out of work and into poverty and hunger, and consequently devastated local coastal communities.

Consumers in industrial countries continue to account for 85% of the value of world fish imports. We now have more than twice the fishing capacity required to harvest the world's oceans sustainably. This simply means that we now have too many fishermen, too many boats and too many hooks and nets taking too many fish out of the sea. Those with larger boats have greater overheads and repayments to make, and often find that their permitted maximum quota is not enough to enable them to break-even – tempting them to land illegally caught fish to make ends meet.

Each species has its own place in the marine food chain. Overfishing of one species can lead another to flourish or decline depending on the place in the food chain of the species being overfished. At the bottom of the food chain, phytoplankton and other plants transform the energy of sunlight into chemical energy. Herbivores then eat these plants and are in turn eaten by small fish, which are then consumed by larger, carnivorous predators such as tuna and sharks at the top of the chain. Crabs are 'carrion eaters' and will eat whatever ends up on the ocean floor, as well as plankton and even smaller fish.

One of the most damaging environmental impacts of modern fishing technology involves trawling techniques that scrape the ocean floor. This is the equivalent of ploughing the seabed in an attempt to flush out bottom-dwelling fish. Weighted trawls have rotating tickler chains that are dragged along the bottom and smash everything in their path, destroying important natural resources like oyster beds.

Most of these productive seabeds are trawled between four and seven times a year. This trawling technique has been compared with strip-mining and clear-cutting of forests, but the scale is far greater. Unfortunately, out of sight means out of mind, so this wanton destruction proceeds unchecked by the industry, unpoliced by the authorities and unnoticed by the consumer.

Removal of more than 90% of the large predatory fish from our oceans has prompted an explosion in the numbers of jellyfish. The Gulf of Thailand in the South China Sea is now being emptied of its fish, but Nature is filling the void with squid and jellyfish. Fishermen from three nations surrounding the Gulf – Cambodia, Vietnam and Thailand – have engaged in lethal battles over the last remaining fish.

The same pattern of decline can be found in Europe, where in 2006, for the first time ever vast numbers of jellyfish populated the Mediterranean. This increase was attributed not only to a rise in water temperature, but also to overfishing of the jellyfish's natural predators such as sea turtles, many of which may have been inadvertently caught and killed by the tuna fishing industry.

As agriculture reduces the flows of cold river water reaching the coastal seas, they remain warmer, which promotes increased jellyfish numbers. Temperature increases in water along the San Diego coastline have resulted in a 70% decline in concentrations of zooplankton. Zooplankton comprises a range of organisms from those too small to see with the naked eye up to small crustaceans such as krill. The decrease in these small creatures at the base of the food chain has led to a corresponding decline in stocks of fish such as sardines and jack mackerel that feed on them.

Pollack (commonly called pollock) is a popular whitefish found in the same breeding grounds as cod and haddock. In the early 1980s, the spawning population of the pollock in waters off Canada was around two million tonnes, and the sea lion population that feeds on them about 20,000 strong. Having fished out the more profitable species, fishermen around the Grand Banks then turned their attention to pollock, reducing its spawning population by 90% to around 230,000 tonnes in just over 20 years — a major factor in the corresponding reduction in the local sea lion population to roughly 3,200.

The loss of sea lions in turn deprives killer whales of their primary food source, with the result that whales are now eating sea otters. The sea otter population has plummeted by 90% since 1990, triggering an explosive growth in sea urchins, previously sea otter prey. In certain areas of the world, sea urchins can then damage coral reefs by eating protective layers of algae.

The total annual global fish catch from marine and inland waters rose dramatically from just over 19 million tonnes in 1950 to over 90 million tonnes by 2009. The UN Food and Agriculture Organisation (FAO) Fisheries Reports of 2010 and (2008), respectively, confirmed that roughly 32% (28%) of global stocks of fish had been either overexploited or depleted. A further 53% (52%) of fish stocks were estimated to be fully exploited. Only 15% (20%) of stocks were assessed as moderately exploited or underexploited. In 2009, the European Commission estimated that 88% of marine fish stocks it monitored were overfished, on the basis of data collected over the last 20 to 40 years.

These overall figures disguise the fact that the most valuable species are the first to be overfished. These valued species are subsequently replaced by catching less desirable species that may have filled the same niche previously occupied by the species that has been wiped out. For instance, following the collapse of the Grand Banks cod fishery in 1992, fishermen started catching dogfish, skate, monkfish and other species that they once would have thrown back overboard as they then had no commercial value.

A similar situation occurred with the West Atlantic bluefin tuna, stocks of which declined by more than 80% between 1970 and 1993. Fishermen from the many nations that targeted tuna switched their efforts to swordfish in an effort to make up for the dwindling catches

89

of the more valuable species. Over this period the average size of swordfish caught on longlines declined from 120 to 30 kilograms, which means that underage stock is being consumed and numbers will therefore continue to decline.

The king of the five commercial tuna species – the bluefin tuna – is an extraordinarily efficient predator that can swim twice round the world in 17 months and reach speeds of up to 70 kilometres per hour as it migrates to spawn and feed. Tuna rely on a constant flow of oxygenated water over their gills to breathe so never stop swimming. They also have a less well-developed swim bladder so cannot regulate their buoyancy, so again must keep swimming. Since it never stops, the bluefin's muscle is continually fed with oxygen by its blood, giving the tuna flesh its distinctive colour. Fish that have well-developed swim bladders like cod tend to have white flesh.

Europe leads the world in tuna consumption, followed by the United States. Fifteen million cans of tuna are consumed every year in the United Kingdom and millions more elsewhere around the world. Pressure on supermarkets from consumers is now having an effect on the way in which tuna is caught, but 'dolphin-friendly' on the can does not mean environmentally friendly.

Fifteen million cans of tuna are consumed every year in the UK alone.

Most tuna fishing is still carried out by a global fleet of some 570 vessels, ranging in size from 250 to 4,000 tonnes. These boats use gigantic purse seine nets in conjunction with Fish Aggregation Devices (FADs), floating platforms tethered to the seabed. These attract smaller fish, which then act as bait for larger fish such as tuna.

Fresh tuna is caught mainly on modern longlines up to 130 kilometres long, which also snare albatrosses, turtles and sharks as they prey on the snared tuna. A more environmentally friendly method is the traditional pole and line – but it is far more labour-intensive.

Atlantic bluefin tuna are among the largest fish in the ocean, some exceeding two metres in length and more than 500 kilograms in weight. Their lifespan can exceed 30 years, making them long-lived compared to other fish species. They take eight years to mature to medium-size breeding fish. Bluefin tuna were rarely caught before the First World War, but the development of intensive fishing methods from the 1920s onwards began the process of depletion. Equipment such as harpoon rifles and hydraulic net lifts helped fishermen increase annual catches from virtually nothing in 1910 to almost 5,500 tonnes of tuna by 1949.

In 1929, Denmark built its first tuna cannery, and by 1949 Norway had 43 boats pursuing tuna, growing to nearly 200 by the peak of the tuna's exploitation. These catches decimated the Atlantic bluefin tuna population between 1910 and 1950. The tuna species virtually disappeared from the region in the early 1960s and is still rare there today.

The total global catch of the five main tuna species expanded from 2.16 million tonnes in 1985 to more than 4 million tonnes in 2008. The main tuna fishing nations today are Taiwan and Japan – who in 2011 called for a global reduction in tuna fishing effort. Bluefin is the world's most expensive fish still available to catch. In January 2011 a near-340 kilogram tuna was sold at Tokyo's Tsukiji market for a phenomenal $396,000 to a restaurant owner.

The main european-based regulatory body is the International Commission for the Conservation of Atlantic Tunas (ICCAT), also glibly known as the International Conspiracy to Catch All Tunas. The heart of ICCAT is a treaty between more than 40 nations. Critics claim that ICCAT does not conserve, but rather presides over the continuing decline and collapse of tuna stocks. Despite endless conferences and scientific studies sponsored by ICCAT, a World Wildlife Fund (WWF) report in 2009 shows that actual catches of bluefin tuna – a critically endangered species – are substantially higher than the quotas set, and that catches are consistently underreported or not reported at all. A complete ban on bluefin tuna-fishing may be the only way to save the species.

Stocks of North Atlantic swordfish – a predatory and migratory fish that can reach two metres in length and up to 650 kilogrammes in weight – were in rapid decline and the species near collapse. Strict international catch quotas agreed in 1999 and a total ban on fishing in their spawning grounds off the coast of the United States have led to a remarkable recovery. ICCAT determined that swordfish had reached 94% of sustainable stock levels by 2004 with a complete recovery expected in due course.

The proposal to ban international trade in Atlantic bluefin tuna has been rejected by the United Nations Convention on International Trade in Endangered Species (CITES) in 2010. The UK, Japan, Canada and several other leading tuna fishing nations opposed the ban on the grounds that it would devastate their fishing economies. Clearly, these nations have not learned from Canada and its grotesque mismanagement of the Grand Banks cod.

Not only do we overfish our seas, but absurd fishing legislation also promotes huge amounts of waste. Regions like the EU set limits on the Total Allowable Catch (TAC) by marine species and by boat or skipper. This quota system specifies the TAC but this really means Total Allowable Landings. Fish landed are recorded, but fish discarded at sea and thrown away are not included in the fisheries' statistics. These discarded fish are known as 'by-catch' and result from observing these limited quotas. If a fisherman, for example, has already filled his quota of cod and is fishing for pollock, any cod he inadvertently catches must be thrown overboard – almost always dead. The TAC policy was ironically designed to conserve stocks and help manage fishing quotas by recording our take from the seas against estimated stocks. It achieves neither of these.

Of the legal cod landed in the UK between 2007 and 2009, as much as a further 50% is thrown away as by-catch from fishing for other species. One North Sea boat was filmed in 2010, and shown on the Fish Fight Campaign, discarding 20 baskets of cod overboard – worth nearly £35,000 and capable of feeding 2,000 people.

Of all marine fish that are legally landed – a further 23% by weight will have been dumped at sea.

Discards are wasteful and damaging: the fish discarded have little or no chance of reviving and at best end up as food for deep-sea crabs. This practice fundamentally undermines the goals of fishery management. The FAO says that no detailed estimate of global by-catch is available, but a crude estimate suggests that it could be more than 20 million tonnes of fish each year. Of all marine fish that are legally landed in port, a further 23% by weight will have been discarded as by-catch at sea.

Fishermen themselves favour other less wasteful methods of managing fishing effort. EU and national officials have been aware of the by-catch problem for decades and are at last considering amending the existing counter-productive regulations in the EU's 2012 fisheries policy review.

This change in fishing policy has largely been brought about by the highly successful 'Fish Fight' campaign led by the UK's celebrity chef and television personality Hugh Fearnley-Whittingstall. This shows again that a committed individual leading a great campaign can deliver change, where inept, well-paid politicians have been incapable of doing so for decades.

93

Probably the only effective method for monitoring fishing activity is by using satellite-tracking systems. This can monitor distance travelled, which will give a good indication of the volume of seas trawled and accurate probable catch. It will also alert port authorities as to the likely time and location of landing of a returning vessel for monitoring purposes. The European Union initially rejected mandating this monitoring method under pressure from its member states, but has now passed legislation that requires all member-state vessels over 12 metres to have installed a Vessel Monitoring System (VMS) by 2012.

Another wasteful practice is 'high grading', a practice that also continues unchecked. High grading is adopted when poor-value fish already caught are discarded to make room for more profitable species. Boat skippers also high grade when they make a good catch at the end of a trip, and discard some of the earlier catch because they are not as fresh. High grading is again driven by quotas on fish that are actually landed at port rather than caught at sea, and again must be banned in the EU fisheries review.

Asia now consumes most of the world's fish. The Japanese eat 66 kilograms of fish per person each year, as opposed to Spain's 44 kilograms and Britain's 20 kilograms per person per year. But at 25 kilograms per person, the Chinese alone eat around a third of the world's fish. The proportion of fish and meat in the Chinese diet is soaring as the population becomes wealthier.

Much of Asia's fish is farmed, as is the world's fish, but this is little consolation.

Large-scale fish farms are essentially aquatic feedlots, comparable in intensity to chicken farming, with hundreds of fish living in cramped conditions. Fish farming largely depends on feeding fishmeal to carnivores such as salmon, trout, shrimp and prawns or omnivores such as tilapia. While there is an increasing use of herbivore and omnivore species in aquaculture, such as catfish and some carp species, these farmed fish are still fed fishmeal as part of their diets to promote growth.

Pelagic fish like anchovies and sardines from the seas around South America are one of the principal components of fishmeal. The production of fishmeal has a direct impact on coastal communities, such as those in Peru. The factories produce both employment and pollution. The city of Chimbote on Peru's coast has 40 fishmeal production facilities, which produce waste effluent poured directly into the sea and chimney smoke causing respiratory problems and skin allergies among many local inhabitants. The costs of producing cheap Scottish and Norwegian-farmed salmon are thus shifted far away to the ecology and social systems of countries like Peru.

The producers of fishmeal claim that their fleets are subject to exemplary environmental protection and conservation management measures: for instance, they do not fish within five miles of a coastline in order to protect the livelihoods of artisan fishermen. According to local fishermen, however, these regulations are simply ignored as they regularly see industrial trawlers near the coast. The regulation of the fishmeal industry has improved dramatically and now ships within the coastal exclusion zones are monitored by satellite-tracking systems and landings monitored for sustainability. Furthermore, the authorities in Peru have now introduced fishing moratoriums in February-March and August-October to protect spawning stocks of anchovies and sardines.

From a total production of less than one million tonnes per year in the early 1950s, by 2006 annual farmed fish production exceeded 50 million tonnes worldwide. Valued at US$78.8 billion, this amounts to almost 50 million tonnes of over one third of man's global fish consumption. This demand-driven farming is developing unchecked, without governments or consumers understanding its detrimental effect on the seas and wild fish populations.

95

World aquaculture is heavily dominated by the Asia-Pacific region, which accounts for 89% of production in terms of quantity and 77% in terms of value. The Asia-Pacific region produces most of the world's carp, oysters, shrimps and prawns. Scotland, Norway and Chile are the leading producers of farmed salmon, whereas sea bass are increasingly farmed in many countries of the world.

In 2009, the FAO estimates that 70% of world marine fish production was used for direct human consumption. The remainder was used in the manufacture of fishmeal and fish oil. With the increase in aquaculture and a decline in high-value wild fish, more low-value and small fish are being used to make fishmeal for farmed fish. Some estimates suggest that by 2015 more than half of the total marine catch will be used in industry and agriculture rather than direct human consumption. Fishmeal is used not only in fish farms, but also as a protein source to feed pigs and poultry.

The world price for fishmeal fluctuated between US$500 and US$700 per tonne between 2000 and 2005, but shot up to US$1,400 in 2006, reaching $1,937 in April 2010. This has led the aquaculture industry to try to lower its dependence on fishmeal.

Some salmon diets, for example, now contain 30% fishmeal as opposed to 50% a few years ago. Salmon are now eating a soya concentrate with added amino acids and maize, as well as off-cuts and trimmings from other fish. Farmed fish are better for supermarkets as they are available in pre-determined sizes as and when required. They are, however, often far worse for the environment. It still takes as much as three kilograms of marine-caught fish to produce one kilogram of farmed salmon. Of this we eat only some 23% – the fillets.

Clean Seas Tuna Ltd in Australia has now bred the first bluefin tuna in captivity. They have invested more

You are better off eating the last fish in the sea than a farmed fish fed on fishmeal.

than US$50 million in this venture, which may in fact be bad news for sea life in general. To produce one kilogram of farmed tuna will probably require almost eight kilograms of fishmeal. As things stand, you are therefore better off eating the last fish in the sea than a farmed fish fed fishmeal from dwindling wild stocks.

Farmed salmon is sold in almost every supermarket, with 1.4 million tonnes now produced annually worldwide — 40 times the amount 20 years ago. Salmon farming is an intensive and highly specialised industry. The United Kingdom's largest salmon farm produces 352,000 tonnes of fish a year. These fish are selectively bred to be short-lived and fast growing, reaching five kilograms in 18 months. In the US, even faster growing genetically modified salmon have now been approved for human consumption.

Farmed salmon have been shown to contain raised levels of contaminants and antibiotics as a result of their concentrated feed and production method. We would actually be better off eating fish like blue whiting, which is often used in producing fishmeal to feed salmon.

So successful has industrial fish farming and selective breeding become that within just seven salmon generations the Norwegians were able to double the salmon growth rate. However, many of these domesticated salmon no longer contain the genetic coding necessary to survive in the wild. Salmon farming in coastal cages is also hugely wasteful, as some of the food they are fed drops through the cages to the seabed. Salmon naturally attract sea lice, which grow on their skin. Removing lice from these caged salmon using chemicals causes unnatural concentrations of sea lice on the floor below their cages. This can affect migratory wild salmon stocks as these cages are often in the river estuaries through which they pass. Combining mussel farming with salmon farming may in time reduce many of the side effects of intense salmon farming. Excess food or lice dropping to the sea floor could be eaten by the mussels.

97

Sea bass aquaculture has been so successful that seven out of eight sea bass eaten are farmed. Israel has pioneered research into farming sea bass since the mid-1980s, with selective breeding having increased edible mass of the now captive genetic strains. Sea bass has become the brand name for a host of farmed white fish that no longer come out of the sea, as their name implies. Farmed sea bass is now as common as farmed salmon. Today Greece exports nearly 100 million plate-sized sea bass to diners throughout the world. The barramundi – marketed as Asian sea bass – is from the same family of fish as sea bass.

Barramundi has the advantage of being predominantly a vegetarian fish. This means that it needs to be fed far less marine-caught fishmeal and could therefore be a more sustainable form of aquaculture. Alongside tilapia, barramundi are the only widely farmed vegetarian fish.

The increasing scarcity of pelagic fish and the subsequent substantial rise in the price of fishmeal have led to the creation of a new fishery – krill harvesting. Krill are small crustaceans near the bottom of the food chain. They are an abundant source of food for ocean fish everywhere, and are particularly abundant in the cold, oxygen-rich polar waters. Perhaps the last of the cheap, easy-to-catch marine protein, they are in demand to make feed for our increasingly industrial fish and shrimp farms.

One Oslo based krill harvester alone landed 8,600 tonnes of krill in the first half of 2010.

This devastating development will impact the whole marine food chain and our seas will suffer. Aker Biomarine – an Oslo-based krill harvester – landed 8,600 tonnes of krill in the first half of 2010 alone. The MSC certified this catch as renewable in May 2010. So little is understood about the complex marine ecosystem and food chain that this must, at best, be irresponsible. In 2010 the global krill catch was expected to reach 180,000 tonnes – up 40% on 2009. The Chinese sent their first krill ship to the Antarctic in 2010 and are expected to rapidly increase their krill fleet. We need urgent, worldwide agreement to ban this practice before it starts in earnest, and to keep this ban in place at least until we understand the impact of our fishing out the beginning of our marine food chain.

Nitrogen fertiliser run-off from fields is combined with urban and industrial waste – including fish farm waste – and flows down rivers into the sea. This effluent causes eutrophication or nutrient enrichment in the estuary seawaters. These nutrients promote algal blooms and oxygen depletion, which create dead zones around these river mouths in which no marine life can exist.

Dead zones continue to grow, and have been doubling every decade since the 1960s, when there were only 49. By 2008, 415 such dead zones were documented around the world, occupying an area of ocean equal to the size of the United Kingdom.

Perhaps the best-known dead zone is in the Mississippi River Delta, running into the Gulf of Mexico and representing an area the size of New Jersey. It is seasonal, as the river carries the fertilisers off the farmland in the rainy season, with the concentration of pollution increased and dispersed by hurricane-season storms. The pollution from the devastating 2010 BP Deep Water Horizon oil spill in the Gulf of Mexico has compounded the problem. The leak released not only oil, but also vast quantities of methane, setting off a chain reaction taking yet more oxygen out of the water. Almost all bottom-dwelling marine organisms have been killed, which has forced local fishermen to venture further offshore to find fish. Worse still, photos taken by NASA in 2010 indicate dead zones spreading along most of the southern and eastern seaboard of the United States.

99

Interestingly, in August 2005 this particular dead zone was partially dispelled by the 130 mile-per-hour winds from Hurricane Katrina, mixing the layers of oxygen-rich and oxygen-depleted waters. In September that year, Hurricane Rita augmented this seawater mixing process, bringing an early end to the seasonal dead zone. Conversely, early summer floods in 2008 washed fertiliser into the Mississippi River from the fields of America's Mid-West, accelerating the formation of that year's dead zone.

The Baltic Sea is the world's largest dead zone. Overfishing of Baltic cod has intensified the problem, because cod eat small fish like sardines (Sprattus), which in turn eat zooplankton, which eat algae. Fewer cod populations have led to an explosion of algae, which consumes the oxygen in the water. Spreading dead zones then engulf the cod's deep-water breeding grounds, compounding the cycle.

On a more hopeful note, the Black Sea during the 1990s was one of the few dead zones to recover. Following the collapse of the Soviet Union, many of the collective or state-run farms failed. This resulted in a massive reduction in farming activity and therefore in fertiliser run-off from fields in Russia and Ukraine.

The UN straddling fishing stocks agreement signed in New York in 1995 is typical of the way in which international treaties function. In 1982 the UN adopted the United Nations Convention on the Law of the Sea (UNCLOS), which provides coastal states with exclusive sovereign rights to conserve and manage fisheries and other rights within 200 nautical miles of their shores. These effectively national waters are called Exclusive Economic Zones (EEZs). The Convention, howver, contained gaps concerning the rights of states regarding highly migratory and straddling fish stocks.

In 1995 a United Nations conference was organised to address these issues. Only 15 nations had ratified the agreed treaty by the end of

1997, 15 short of the number required to make the treaty binding under international law. Only 4 of the 20 major fishing nations – the United States, the United Kingdom, Russia and Norway – had signed the treaty. It was not until 2001 that it finally took effect. In May 2010 many of the signatory countries met in Canada to discuss the implementation and policing of the 1995 agreement. No new concrete measures were agreed to, however, and while the agreement is binding its implementation remains ineffective.

In the mid-1990s, the EU set aside US$2.2 billion to fund restructuring of the fishing industry and economic transition programmes to enable fishermen to retrain in other professions. Such was the pressure from fishermen, industry officials and national politicians that the EU backed down on proposed fleet reductions and continued to postpone necessary reforms. The EU continues to provide funds and support for fleet modernisation and upgrading to 'maintain competitiveness' rather than reduce the massive and subsidised fishing overcapacity.

The only practical solution for saving our seas is the creation of marine reserves or marine protected areas (MPAs). We protect large parts of our wilderness through national parks, but have largely ignored the protection of our seas. Wherever they have been introduced, marine reserves have benefited the fishing industry: fish are given the space to breed and reproduce, and when they become too dense they migrate to areas where they can be legally caught.

Where marine reserves have already been established, such as off St Lucia in the Caribbean, protected fish stocks have increased five to tenfold in a decade. Vast areas of Georges Bank off the eastern United States were protected from bottom trawling and scallop dredging in 1994: within 10 years, stocks of scallops had increased by 250% in the closed areas, while yellowtail, flounder and haddock also recovered. Since large invertebrates are not subjected to the periodic destructive activity of bottom trawls, a range of invertebrates was

101

also re-established on the seabed. Marine reserves work and they work quickly, benefiting both the fishing industry and fish stocks: we just need more of them, and now.

Coastal nations agreed to create marine reserves to cover 10% of the worlds oceans by 2012 – but are failing to deliver on this promise.

Johannesburg, South Africa, hosted the 2002 World Summit on Sustainable Development at which coastal nations agreed to create marine reserves that would cover 10% of the world's oceans by 2012. A further UN summit on the environment and climate change (COP 17) will be hosted by the city of Durban in December 2011, at which many of the same countries and their leaders will be present. By then as little as 1% of the oceans will be covered by reserves and many of those are poorly controlled and still allow fishing.

A 2004 survey by the Conservation Science Group at Cambridge University calculated the annual maintenance and patrolling costs of an international marine reserve network covering 30% of the oceans at between £7 billion and £8.2 billion per year, compared with the £17.6 billion a year we currently spend on subsidies that actually promote overfishing. These reserves need to be under independent jurisdiction, because industrial-political control of regulatory bodies has not worked in the past, repeatedly succumbing to short-term financial or political pressure. An independent body like a Reserve Bank, with a clear mandate, is likely to make strategic, long-term decisions and restore marine ecosystems to a state of far greater health and abundance. The global protection of boundary-less species – including absolute bans on the fishing of certain species such as bluefin tuna – should be part of its mandate.

The European Commission in its 2007 communication on fishing capacity suggested a reduction in fleet size and a dramatic cut in fishing effort among a raft of measures to improve sustainability of the

EU's fisheries. A repeal of the EU's TAC laws that promote by-catch and the regulation of bottom trawling would be sensible starting points. Experts argue that any changes must include funding for the creation of Marine Protected Areas (MPAs). We need a profound reduction in fishing effort. This means conservative limits on fisheries well below the maximum sustainable yield, and eating less marine-caught fish and more 'vegetarian' farmed fish.

Unlike TAC's in European waters, Individual Transferable Quotas (ITQs) have been proposed by marine conservation bodies as an equitable way of managing fisheries and have been successfully implemented in a number of countries, including Iceland, the Netherlands and New Zealand. ITQs give the owner the right to harvest a fixed amount or percentage of fish in a particular area and over a particular time period. Since quotas can be bought and sold on the market, less efficient fishermen can sell the quotas on to someone else. In practice, this has led to consolidation of quotas in the hands of the largest players, with a corresponding adverse effect on small-scale local fishermen. In business, too, big fish consume the smaller ones.

Consumers have the MSC to look to for guidance as to which fish they should eat. When the UK's fisheries minister Richard Benyon, however, was asked in an impromptu test in 2010 to identify the UK's 12 most common sea fish, laid out on a fishmonger's slab, he came up short. He could name only cod, monkfish and pollock – of the other nine common species he was unable to name fish such as haddock and plaice. Few of us know exactly what fish we are eating, but a fisheries minister should at least recognise the fish he is charged with managing.

Fisheries form a complex web of relationships that include ecological, scientific, social, economic, political and technological factors, which often pull in different directions. It is difficult to reconcile these interests simultaneously.

103

There is general agreement among scientists, the fishing industry and politicians that deep-water fish stocks are over-exploited. Political imperatives from local employment to long-standing traditions mitigate against government action. Inconsistencies in different scientific assessment are not unusual where scientists cannot see what they are counting, have little idea of what is actually being taken from the seas, and have limited understanding as yet of the complex marine ecosystems. Even though all the findings point towards varying degrees of over-exploitation, government uses the inconsistencies in the extent of the declines to postpone the urgent action required. This includes the delayed implementation of internationally agreed conservation methods such as the establishment of MPA's. These calls for all shades of scientific opinion to be considered are just a thinly disguised form of deceit by politicians and the fishing industry to justify business-as-usual – rather than acting to solve the problem.

During the 1970s the plight of the whales first came to broader public attention. A number of conservation organisations particularly in the US, including the then nascent Greenpeace, lobbied governments and took direct action to prevent whaling. Public awareness globally increased, and 'Save the Whales" car bumper stickers and t-shirts appeared in many countries. The International Whaling Commission finally bowed to member-state pressure and a moratorium on whaling was adopted in 1982, taking effect in 1986. The world moved together to save the whales and won.

Swordfish became a popular restaurant dish as awareness of the plight of tuna increased, but eventually swordfish were also being over-exploited. The 1998 US-based campaign 'Give the Swordfish a Break' arose from an unusual alliance between two environmental organisations, the Natural Resources Defense Council and SeaWeb, and some of the nation's finest chefs. In 1995 an estimated 58% of the Atlantic swordfish catch was of immature fish. Following public pressure swordfish fishing was banned in US waters and strict

Swordfish fishing was banned in US waters and strict international quotas imposed in open waters – stocks are now recovering and the species is recovering from the brink of extinction.

international quotas imposed in open seas in 1994. As a result, swordfish stocks have recovered and the species removed from the brink of extinction.

As far back as the 1980s, a consumer boycott of canned tuna in the United States forced changes in the way in which tuna was caught and so helped protect dolphins and other by-catch. Morrissons was the latest UK supermarket to cave in to pressure not to source its tuna using FAD and purse-sein catch methods. It caved in to consumer pressure in 2011 and agreed not to stock source tuna caught by this method from 2013. We now need to support the campaigns to suspend and ban tuna fishing altogether to allow stocks to recover.

The current consumer pressure on by-catch in Europe is prompting legislative change and increasing awareness of our oceans. There are current campaigns to create a network of International Marine Reserves. Both initiatives can be supported online, and should be.

We can save our seas and preserve our marine life for future generations. We need committed individuals to lead the fight against ignorant and incompetent governments and greedy fishing industry executives. Governments must do what they are paid to do: plan for our common and sustainable future.

CHAPTER FOUR – **POPULATION**

In 1792, the Reverend Thomas Robert Malthus was struck by the fact that in his first three years of ministry in Surrey, England, he had officiated at 57 births but only 12 deaths. In 1798 he published the first edition of his *Essay on the Principles of Population,* in which he argued that man's capacity to increase food production was lower than our rate of population growth – especially among the poor. This he believed would lead inexorably to a population disaster.

What he referred to as the positive checks of famine and disease would, he believed, bring about a drastic cull in human numbers. Furthermore, he took the view that giving charity to the poor was against the laws of Nature and harmful in the long term since charity would only postpone an even larger eventual population crash.

British policy towards the Irish Potato Famine of 1842 reflected Malthus' view. It encouraged a hands-off attitude that led to the eventual death of hundreds of thousands of people. Opponents of Malthus' delight in observing that he has so far been proven wrong and that population growth has not led to mass starvation.

Malthus later tempered his original bleak outlook, proposing universal suffrage and state-run education to inculcate what amounted to middle-class virtues for all. Good education and rising living standards generally promote a decline in the birth rate.

Early humans faced many challenges, from finding sufficient food to battling with predators – survival was a continual struggle. Archaeological remains indicate that there was a relatively stable world population with a high birth rate balanced by high, mainly infant, mortality. It is estimated that the human population in 10,000 BC was approximately 6 million people, with an average life expectancy of just 20 years.

For thousands of years, the survival of early man depended on this high birth rate. Even with the population doubling every few thousand years, it was not until 2000 BC that the world's population reached 100 million.

By the time of Christ the world's population had increased to 250 million, but life expectancy was still only 22 years. The Black Death pandemic eliminated a third of the European population or nearly 25 million people in the 14th century, but by 1750 the global population had grown to 770 million and life expectancy has increased to 27 years. A population of one billion people was reached around 1800, and it took almost another 130 years to reach two billion. In the two centuries between 1800 and 2000 we added four billion people to the planet. Between 2000 and 2050, world population will increase by a further three billion people to peak at just over nine billion people.

It is only in the last two centuries that this exponential population growth has led us to question the number of humans the planet can sustainably support – its carrying capacity. It is estimated that the sustainable carrying capacity of our Earth and its natural systems is between two and three billion people.

Advances in health care over the last century have reduced deaths without affecting the birth rate. With better birth control and wider access to family planning, birth rates have recently started to decline.

The discovery of oil, the invention of the internal combustion engine in the late 19th century, widespread mechanisation of agriculture and the development of fertilisers have increased land yields. The use of non-renewable fossil resources has enabled a far larger number of people to be fed, contributing to the current population bubble.

... the only day in recent history the world's population did not increase was the 26th December 2004 – when the Indian Ocean tsunami struck fourteen countries.

Two significant peaks in population growth statistics have already been reached: the largest annual percentage increase of 2.2% occurred in 1962, and the record for the most people added in one year peaked at 88 million in 1989. This means that the only day in recent history the world's population did not increase was the 26th December 2004, when the Indian Ocean tsunami struck 14 countries. Despite the scale of this tragedy – with more than 230,000 deaths – the total global population was only reduced slightly as there were also over 200,000 net births that day.

By 2050, the annual rate of global population increase is expected to have 'dropped' to 41 million people per year. The world's population by then is projected to have reached 9.2 billion, up from its current 6.9 billion people.

The earliest indications of a potential population explosion came in the '40s when healthcare improvements led to a demonstrable reduction in mortality rates. Forecasters at that time and up until the '60s suggested that food production would not be able to keep up with the continually growing population, and mass starvation would result from this imbalance.

Like Malthus before them, proponents of these dire forecasts have continually been proven wrong, as man's inventiveness has broadly enabled food production to keep pace with population growth. The Green Revolution, with its industriallsation of agriculture, fertilisers and genetically modified crops, has had a profound impact on agricultural yields. Without these technological developments in food production, hundreds of millions of people would indeed have starved to death.

Population growth in itself does not give a full picture of the impact of man on the planet. Many people assume that the most important figure is the absolute number of people on the planet, but the level of their consumption and the pollution caused in producing that consumption give a far better depiction of our real impact on the environment.

For example, commuting to work in a petrol-driven sports utility vehicle (SUV) has a far greater impact on the environment than using a bicycle or, indeed, even working from home. One person living on the poverty line in a developing nation consumes far less from the environment than their Western counterpart.

The resource consumption of one American is equivalent to that of 40 Africans. Consequently, a population increase of 100,000 people in the United States (US) has the same impact on the environment as an increase of four million people in Africa. In terms of comparative resource demand, Sweden, with just over nine million people in 2010, used 15 times more resources than Bangladesh with its far larger population of 162 million.

In a world where growing affluence has been a gradual and long-term trend, each person we add to the planet will probably cause more environmental damage than any of their predecessors. More and more people from rapidly developing countries like India and China are adopting 'American' or consumption-driven lifestyle aspirations. Indeed, consumption increasingly defines our human identity: we are becoming the brands that we eat, use and wear.

Put simply, the crisis we face is that we are too many people consuming too many of the natural resources available to us. For the world population to consume goods – and therefore the environment – at the rate of the richest 10% of the population, we would need four planet Earths.

Technological advances in agriculture, manufacturing and recycling have been extraordinary but will not allow population and the economy to grow forever. We therefore face some difficult choices as the realities of finite natural resources feed into price mechanisms.

Most politicians – and many economists – still regard consumption as sacrosanct, as a cure-all for economic growth, and vital to their re-election. The modern world measures its success and development in terms of increasing its output as measured in financial terms by Gross Domestic Product (GDP). The real challenge, however, is for developed countries is to find a way of increasing prosperity without economic growth and for developing countries to advance their prosperity without a corresponding increase in environmental impact.

In 1972, King Wangchuck of Bhutan first proposed an alternative to GDP as a measure for a society's progress. His proposal introduced a broader concept – Gross National Happiness or GNH – as a measure of progress. GNH looks at many aspects of social well-being from good governance to sustainable development and the environment. Some 30 years later in November 2010, the British Prime Minister David Cameron proposed measuring happiness as an indicator for prosperity in the United Kingdom, rather than just its physical output of goods and services measured by GDP.

Developed countries are already overusing resources, while more than 15% of our human population still live below the poverty line. The rich are already consuming the water of the thirsty, eating the food of the hungry and burning the fuel of the cold.

The rich are already consuming the water of the thirsty, eating the food of the hungry and burning the fuel of the cold.

United Nations (UN) statistics on consumption show that the wealthiest 20% of the world's population consumes 86% of the world's resources while the poorest 20% consume just a meagre 1.3%. It has always been the case that it is easier to accumulate wealth if you already have disposable income, education and opportunity: the already-rich and their children tend to become wealthier and the poor simply become poorer.

111

Not everyone agrees that population increase is a problem. In his writings on population growth, the late Professor Julian Simon, a former professor of business and economics at the Universities of Maryland and Illinois, regarded people as "the ultimate resource" (the title of his 1981 book): not just more mouths to feed, but more hands as well as more minds to solve man's problems. He argued that natural resources are not finite, but are created by man's intellect, which is a continually renewable resource. With the huge advances in recycling, energy and food production there is substantial merit in this viewpoint.

Recycling of everything from paper to cars has increased exponentially across the globe in the last few decades. New European Union (EU) legislation even mandates that new products be manufactured in such a way that they can be easily broken down into recyclable parts. This means that, in future, EU manufacturers will have to take back their own used goods for recycling. Huge increases in renewable energy investment, from wind to solar to geothermal, are defining how we will power our planet. New and improved genetically modified (GM) foodstuffs from corn to salmon – as well as hydroponic or soil-free growth technologies – are improving our food production capacity by the day.

It is important to realise, however, that it is mainly the rich and those in the Western world who have access to the technology required to recycle scarce resources, produce food efficiently and develop sustainable power sources. The application of man's intellect is therefore constrained by economics and access to capital. While man may indeed create many ways of using and re-using resources, some natural resources are undeniably finite and non-renewable.

Others may argue that poverty rather than affluence is the environment's primary enemy. In terms of environmental impact, however, this is not necessarily correct: certainly desperate people have no alternative but to chop down trees to cook their food or overgraze marginal land with goats in order to feed themselves, but over-consumption has an equally devastating impact.

Unless we can find ways of bringing population growth and over-consumption under control, our planet's life support systems will continue to deteriorate. There are many signs that our environmental systems are already failing – from water shortages to floods, immense fires and dust storms across the world. Focusing on this failure leads many to ignore the issues, as too much environmental news is doom and gloom. Many of the great things that we are doing to save the environment – from rehabilitating the Loess Plateau in China to building solar power stations in the US – are underreported because good news does not make headlines.

Each of us, however, interprets these predominantly negative messages in accordance with our temperament or outlook. There are five main types of viewpoints, ranging from optimistic to pessimistic. The optimistic and technology-oriented suggest that human ingenuity will triumph. The more pessimistic suggest that you can't change human nature, and that there is no sign of the significant pre-emptive action required to restore the environment.

It is hard to ignore the planet's significant population increase over the last few decades. Wherever you live and go there seem to be more people. The continuing increase in world population masks considerable regional population variations as well as the immense divide between rural and urban populations. More than four billion people now live in Asia, while China and India alone account for 41% of current world population. This is more than the combined populations of Africa, Europe, North America and Latin America. HIV has had a moderating and hopefully temporary restraining effect on population numbers. At the end of 2009 there were 22.5 million people living with HIV/AIDS in Sub-Saharan Africa, where it has already killed 1.3 million people.

At the end of 2009 there were 22.5 million people living with HIV/AIDS in Sub-Saharan Africa, where it has already killed 1.3 million people.

113

While Asia and Africa are growing their share of world population, Europe's population is shrinking both as a percentage of world's population and as an absolute number. These differing growth rates will change the distribution of the world population by 2050.

By 2050 it is estimated that the population of Africa will more than double to nearly two billion people. At the same time there will also be more than five billion people in Asia. As the African population grows they will surely want back their land and water resources that the Chinese and Middle East are currently buying and using to feed their respective populations. As a result, Africa may well be home to many of the resource and food wars of the future.

The population of Europe, however, will have declined from 727 million to 691 million. Since German reunification, births in the former East Germany plummeted from 216,000 in 1988 to only 88,000 in 1994. Many younger people from former Eastern Bloc countries have migrated to the West to seek employment opportunities and better living standards. This reduction in population, combined with falling childbirth rates across Europe, is leading to structural population issues, including declining workforces and increasing numbers of elderly people who require care.

In Russia this demographic crisis is even more acute, with the average life expectancy of men falling from a peak of 67 to its current level of 59 years of age. With its current birth rates, Russia will experience a decline in population from 142 million in 2010 to an estimated 103 million by 2050. Yemen is at the other end of the population-change spectrum. In 1950 Yemen's population was only five million, but today it exceeds 23 million and is expected to reach Russia's population of 103 million by 2050.

The average birth rate in order to maintain a numerically stable global population is around 2.1 children per woman. This population replacement rate is higher where there are increased mortality rates, as in much of Africa. Since Europe's post-war baby boom, the average age at which European women have their first child has risen from 24 to 29, and in most European countries overall birth rates have dropped to below 1.5 and therefore well below the population replacement rate.

Given these birth rates, Europe will have a completely new demography by the end of the 21st century. Italy and Germany have the lowest birth rates in Europe at 1.4 births per female. This is below the population replacement rate and means that, over time, their populations will decline. Extrapolating these birth rate figures over the coming decades means that by the end of this century Italy will have lost a staggering 86% of its current population and Germany 83%. Within this decline, however, some sectors of their immigrant population are growing and will continue to grow. Migration and immigration will temper these figures for European population loss, as young people move from Eastern Europe and North Africa to work and live in countries like Italy and Germany.

In 2006, immigration to EU countries from Morocco and Ukraine alone totalled 250,000 people. The average age of the immigrants was 27. In addition, more than three million people moved within the 27 EU countries in that same year – mostly from the east to the larger and wealthier countries of the west.

A 2011 report from the Pew Charitable Trusts, a non-profit public policy foundation based in the United States, forecasts that globally the Muslim population will grow at twice the rate of the non-Muslim populations over the next 20 years. In Europe as a whole, 8% of the population is expected to be Muslim by 2030. It is unlikely that there will actually be such a steep decline in overall European population numbers, as economic and environmental migration will replace much of this loss.

Birth rates are the most critical variable in determining the size of future global population. A marginal increase in birth rates above or below replacement rates will over two generations – 60 years – have a material impact on actual populations. A United Nations (UN) sensitivity analysis was conducted in 1990, with world population then at 5.3 billion. It showed that just 0.1 added to, or taken off, the replacement birth rate of 2.1 children per woman implied a huge disparity: a global population of either 7.8 billion or one of 12.5 billion by 2050. A birth rate of 3.0 translates into a population increasing in size by 20 times in just 100 years.

Advances in contraceptive techniques, education and the sexual revolution of the 1960s have combined to create a new dynamic of more sex but less procreation. We can better understand the effect of contraception on our population by looking at some statistics of a day of reproduction on our planet from the 2008 Durex World Sex Survey and the 2010 United Nations World Health Report.

Across the world on an average day, 100 million acts of sexual intercourse take place, yielding 910,000 conceptions. More than 150,000 abortions are performed and 369,000 babies born; 1,870 mothers die of pregnancy-related issues; and 39,000 children under four years old die. The net result is that the world's population increases by more than 200,000 that day.

Across the world on an average day, 100 million acts of sexual intercourse take place, 369,000 babies are born and the world's population increases by more than 200,000 people.

A 2003 UN report on world contraceptive use estimated that two-thirds of couples in the world used some form of contraception, with higher usage rates in the developed world. Around a quarter of the 135 million annual births are still unplanned, which leaves considerable scope for further reducing overall birth rates.

Women in relatively more liberated developing countries like India or Brazil are increasingly free to pursue their own ambitions and career, postponing marriage and no longer feeling socially obliged to have children. As a result birth rates in these countries are falling. However, a substantial number of women in less developed countries like Pakistan and Bangladesh still do not have access to adequate family planning services.

In India, where sterilisation is the main form of contraception, the average age for sterilisation of women is now 26 years of age. In Uganda 700,000 men are expected to enrol in its government's three-year vasectomy programme starting in 2011. The health ministry is running this programme in a bid to reduce the country's birth rate from the current 2.7.

The overall global picture is one of declining birth rates from an average of over five children per woman in the 1950s to 3.9 in the late 1970s, 2.8 in 2000 and 2.6 by 2008. This is approaching the global population replacement birth rate of 2.1, and already more than 60 countries with nearly half the world's population have birth rates below their national replacement levels.

In all countries, but particularly in the developing world, birth rates in cities are far below those of rural areas. People in rural areas are less likely to have access to contraception and abortion facilities than their urban counterparts. On many farms, children help with the livestock and other farming chores. In cities children tend to be an economic liability rather than an asset as they are unable to contribute to the economic activity of their parents. Cities may well be the best form of contraceptive man has invented to date.

In 2008, the World Bank calculated that the world's middle class would expand from 430 million in 2000 to 1.15 billion by 2030. The middle class in the Western world is relatively stable; it is in the developing world where people are moving rapidly out of poverty. The globally accepted poverty line in developing countries is an income of US$2 per day. Middle-class income earners are defined as those people earning between US$8 and US$20 a day. This gives these people disposable income after having met their basic requirements of food and shelter.

In 2000, 56% of the global middle class lived in developing countries, but that figure will reach 93% by 2030. Of the 700 million new middle class forecast, at least 350 million will be Chinese. Despite this rapid growth, the global middle class accounted for only 6% of the world's population in 2005, and in 2030 this will still be only 15%.

China and India will have over 40% of the world's middle class by 2030, whereas they had virtually none in 2000. These middle-class people aspire to, and will increasingly be able to afford, Western consumer goods and living standards. They will consume more meat and fish, which will indirectly exert more pressure on grain supply and lead to price increases. Additional demand for water for soda drinks and the manufacture of consumer goods will further strain water supplies.

Coca-Cola's chief executive, Muhtar Ken, believes this new, emerging middle class is critical to the company's future. In 2008 he described the scale of the opportunity as the equivalent, in consumer purchasing terms, of adding a city the size of New York to the world every three months. China is already the world's largest market for television sets and cell phones, as well as the second largest market for cars and personal computers.

Below middle-class income levels there are a rapidly increasing number of people graduating from the US$2 - $6 a day income bracket up to US$6 - $12 a day. The momentum from lower-income groups also supports the forecast demographic of an expanding middle class.

Urbanisation has accelerated since 1950 when less than a third of people lived in cities. Now for the first time more than 50% of the world population lives in urban environments. This number is set to grow as more young people in search of opportunity migrate to the slums of our rapidly developing cities. In 1950 there were 86 cities with populations exceeding one million inhabitants. By 2005 there were 400 such cities and, according to the International Institute for Environmental Development (IIED), it is anticipated that there will be over 550 by 2015.

In 1950 there were 86 cities with populations exceeding one million inhabitants. By 2005 there were 400 such cities and ... it is anticipated that there will be over 550 by 2015.

Total rural populations are set to decline from 2020, so the anticipated net population increase will be in the urban populations of developing countries. Some of the largest of these cities – Dhaka, Kinshasa and Lagos – already have populations 40 times the size they were in the 1950s. Mexico City, Seoul and Sao Paulo have grown to megacity status with around 20 million inhabitants each. Existing megacities are still growing: by 2025 Mumbai is expected to have reached 33 million inhabitants and Shanghai 27 million.

Since the 1970s, more than 200 million Chinese have migrated to their cities and a further 300 million are expected to follow by 2050. The cost of this migration has been a vast expansion of slum populations as cities have failed to adapt to population influx and develop formal infrastructure quickly enough.

Sao Paolo's slums or *favelas* comprised just 1.2% of the city's population in 1973, accelerating rapidly to make up over a quarter of the population by the mid '90s. Of the 500,000 people who migrate to Delhi every year, over 80% end up living in its slums. Delhi's slum

119

population is expected to reach ten million by 2015. Africa is expected to have 332 million slum dwellers by the same year, a figure that is expected to double by 2042, by which time almost a third of Africa's population will be slum dwellers. Globally, over one billion people, one third of the current urban population, live in slums.

The sheer concentration of large numbers of people in overcrowded slum conditions gives rise to a number of health and social problems that can only get worse. Over the course of the 20th century earthquakes destroyed 100 million homes, disproportionately affecting slum housing. Slum cities are also more vulnerable to the destructive forces of floods and fire. Rapid motorisation and poor public transport has exacerbated air pollution, with over a million new cars registered in Delhi in 2006.

One of the most serious challenges in slums is waste disposal, including human waste, where often only the crudest sanitary arrangements are available. Kinshasa, with nearly ten million inhabitants, lacks even a basic sewage system – which means people are living with their own excrement. By necessity an estimated 700 million Indians defecate outside their homes, and women in Mumbai tend to relieve themselves between two and five in the morning so as to ensure some privacy.

Poor or non-existent sanitation or waste disposal promotes widespread contamination of water and food leading to a corresponding increase in disease and illness. Health in slum cities will continue to deteriorate unless there is a material investment in sanitation.

Slum dwellers cannot grow their own food because there is simply no

Many of the countries with the fastest growing populations in the world also face the most difficult environmental challenges.

space. They are, therefore, particularly vulnerable to increases in the price of food and fresh drinking water. Scarce water supply in many slum cities can make water more expensive than in wealthy Western cities. The World Food Programme warns that rising food prices will force many urban poor to reduce their protein consumption. The poorest of the poor will be hardest hit. In 2007/8 worldwide food price increases caused protests and riots in over 30 countries.

It looks increasingly likely that further price increases and their associated protests will happen again in 2011 – perhaps on an even more alarming scale. The current drought in the US grain belt has prompted a price rise of 8% for grain in the month of April 2011 alone.

The 2008 price surge pushed 100 million people further into poverty, according to Robert Zoellick, president of the World Bank. The task of providing relief to those people most in need is complicated by the fact that many future food crises will affect large urban areas, rather than the localised and mainly rural famines of the past.

With rural hunger the key issues are food supply, improved sanitation (to reduce the risk of spreading disease) and healthcare for the undernourished. In urban settings hunger is more likely to lead to riots. The density of population in cities makes sanitation improvements difficult to deliver, and migration – often a consequence of rural famine – is unlikely.

Many of the countries with the fastest-growing populations in the world also face the most difficult environmental challenges, such as rapid groundwater depletion and soil erosion. As their governments struggle to deal with the seemingly irreconcilable problem of more people and fewer resources, they either ignore the issue or give up.

121

These countries then become prone to violent internal conflict and subsequent political and social disintegration, and are termed failing or failed states. We are seeing this in parts of North Africa (Somalia and Sudan) and the Middle East (Iraq and Yemen) as we write.

The UN Food and Agriculture Organisation (FAO) maintains a list of 37 countries currently in crisis, many of which already require external food assistance. Eight of these countries have required UN peacekeeping intervention. The total population of these countries in crisis was 1.1bn in 2010 and is projected to be almost double by 2050. Other countries like Egypt and Libya may extend this list in 2011.

Many of these countries at risk also have young populations. Ethiopia has a population with over 40% under the age of 15. This indicates not only the demographic potential for further rapid population expansion, but also for political unrest resulting from a disaffected youth with limited opportunities.

Many states currently at risk like Pakistan, have progressed far enough to reduce mortality through healthcare but have not invested sufficiently in education and family planning, for financial or religious reasons, to reduce birth rates. This creates a vicious circle of large families which perpetuate poverty through their inability to support themselves.

Failing countries like Afghanistan and Ethiopia struggle with domestic issues such as lack of personal security or lack of opportunity for their young people. Afghanistan and Yemen are known for being lawless and for harbouring terrorist organisations. Countries like Somalia pose security threats to other nations, as we have seen with Somali pirates hijacking merchant and private ships in coastal waters. Where failing states share river or other ecosystems with neighbouring states, environmental damage is more likely to be exported as a result of ineffective control or lack of regulation.

Western military and peacekeeping interventions in such countries have been common. In order to reduce budget deficits, military cutbacks are currently being planned across Europe and in the US. Increasing domestic pressure not to fund military ventures overseas is reducing the West's desire and ability to intervene in failing countries. The recent reticence of the US to intervene in Libya and the first ever presence of a Chinese warship in the Mediterranean Sea may prove to be the beginning of a change in the relative positioning of these two superpowers on the world stage. Unlike the West, China is expanding its military capacity. Its navy is increasingly used to protect its sea routes to trading partners and commodity suppliers in Africa – much as the US did in the past. China's presence in Africa already dwarfs that of the US: in the scramble for Africa's commodities it is likely that the Chinese will play a pivotal role in Africa's failing states. Ideally, any such interventions will learn from past mistakes. Peacekeeping or military interventions must be supplemented by education and family planning services, as well as environmental sustainability programmes, as part of a balanced recovery strategy.

We have seen major economic migrations over the last few hundred years, but nothing will compare with the environmental migrations that will start in the coming decades.

We have seen major economic migrations over the last few hundred years, but nothing will compare with the environmental migrations that will start in the coming decades. Already Yemen is running out of water – where will its 50 million people move to when its aquifers finally run dry? Such a migration could create the first slums around Dubai and other modern Middle Eastern cities.

123

What is the carrying capacity of the Earth? The answer depends on human choices and lifestyles: how we balance growing human needs with limited resources. The answer to these twin challenges lies in 'sustainable development'. This means defining the type, pace and consequent impact of our development on natural systems such as water, land and the seas.

The World Bank calculates that demand for food in developing countries has increased more than threefold over the last 40 years and will do so again in the next 20 years. We already grow enough food to feed a population of 9 billion, if only we did not feed half the current world cereal output to livestock or convert it into fuel.

People often refer to the need for consumption by the richer countries to decline, but if this happens on a large scale, those economies will go into recession, with all its attendant economic, political and social problems. With a scenario of rising population and consumption, economic and political decision makers will simultaneously face the urgent, multiple, and interrelated problems of conservation, resource substitution and technological innovation.

We have yet to formulate an economic system that does not depend on growth for its stability, and yet this very growth means further consumption of limited resources and causes its self destruction. We have not yet worked out how to prosper without growth or to share the resources we have. We fall back to the market system that has served much of humanity well over the last 100 years.

These markets use price to balance supply and demand. Relative incomes and wealth

We currently rely on capitalism to allocate hunger, starvation and death. Charity simply interrupts this otherwise frighteningly efficient process. Can we allow this to continue?

then determine how much of the world's resources an individual or nation can consume. When this relates to food, the populations of poorer nations end up hungrier and more malnourished than those of wealthier nations. We currently rely on capitalism to allocate hunger, starvation and death. Charity simply interrupts this otherwise frighteningly efficient process. Can we allow this to continue?

CHAPTER FIVE – **THE AGRI-INDUSTRY AND ANIMAL CITIES**

Our global food system is becoming increasingly dysfunctional. It produces 20% more calories per capita than we need to feed our forecast peak population, yet leaves many people hungry. A quarter of our global population is undernourished, hungry or starving whilst a similar number are overweight or obese.

Approximately 25,000 people a day die of malnutrition and starvation, whilst 25% of all deaths in the European Union (EU) are recorded with obesity as an underlying cause of death. Our planet is both stuffed and starved.

Without drastic action, our food system will deteriorate even further. Concerted action to overhaul the system is frustrated by competing power structures and political agendas, each with their vested interests.

Despite the founding of the Food and Agriculture Organisation (FAO) and the World Health Organisation (WHO) by the United Nations (UN) over 60 years ago, we still fail to manage health and agriculture as the interlinked systems that they actually are. Our food supply has increased in line with our population, and yet this food system still fails to deliver appropriate nutrition to one-third of the world's population.

The total number of undernourished people has actually increased over the last 15 years from a low of 788 million in 1996 to over one billion in 2010. With record food price increases being logged and oil prices continuing to hover around US$100 per barrel, the number of hungry people worldwide will increase. The food markets are not functioning effectively in service of our global population. Most agricultural produce markets are not free, but politically distorted by production subsidies or unequal national regulation and do not function properly. The short-term quarterly profit focus of the global multinational businesses operating in this food system reduces its sustainability.

127

While the poor do not have enough money to pay for basic foodstuffs, the wealthy in developed countries are persuaded to consume large quantities of addictive junk food products. It may seem a contradiction that overeating these foods can lead to malnutrition: junk food has too many calories but too few nutrients, with the result that people are overfed yet undernourished. Even the stuffed are in this sense also starved.

There are five key interlinked elements that make up our global food system: human health; the business of agriculture; consumer culture; the environment; and food governance. The current emphasis on economic growth and trade liberalisation seeks to maximise short-term profits for farmers and companies. In our capitalist food system, commerce prevails over ecology and growth over sustainability. This philosophy has led not only to a credit crunch but will also lead to an environmental crunch as we are drawing down on Nature's finite capital reserves.

Just as over the last 60 years we have seen a substantial migration of people from the country to the towns, so the food system has moved from being rural and agricultural to urban and industrial. This change has had huge implications for how we buy our food and what we actually eat.

In rural areas, the food supply chain should be quite short. Local farmers replant their own seeds, harvest crops themselves and distribute them locally through markets and shops. This, however, is far from reality: the global, urbanised food chain in the developed world is much longer, and food sometimes travels vast distances via centralised depots only to return and be displayed on the shelves of shops near where it originated.

Food sometimes travels huge distances via centralised depots to end up back on shelves near where it originated.

There are seven main activities in this global food chain. It starts with the supply of agricultural inputs such as grain and genetically modified (GM) seeds, fertilisers and pesticides. Then there is the primary production of food by farmers from grain to meat and fish from aquaculture or fishermen. Primary food processing begins on the farm – for example in dairies, abattoirs and grain mills. Secondary food processing – such as canning and freezing, ready meal and drink preparation – is done in factories. This food is then distributed, transported and traded nationally and internationally. The penultimate step is food retailing in supermarkets and shops, or food catering in restaurants, hotels, schools and hospitals before we finally see food in the home.

In the modern food supply chain, the power no longer lies with farmers. Food processors, traders and retailers focus on owning consumer loyalty and a share of the consumer's wallet. The food processing industry has developed a sophisticated capacity to manipulate our food purchases, while at the same time making sure we take the blame for food choices that may lead to our poor health through, for example, obesity.

Business mergers have produced ever more powerful food and agricultural companies. Food policy is core to their business and strategic planning. Most large companies therefore become actively involved in lobbying government to foster policy decisions that will permit and benefit their commercial activities.

In local rural food systems, with the re-emergence of farmers' markets and vegetable box distribution, the farmer receives a larger proportion of the retail price. In a globalised market system, however, farmers' margins are squeezed due to the massive purchasing power wielded by giant corporations and supermarkets.

Fifty years ago, North American farmers received between 40 and 60 cents of every dollar spent by consumers; the average today is less than 4 cents. Across the world agricultural system, the story is similar. For every £1 worth of Ecuadorian bananas delivered to the United Kingdom, the plantation worker receives under 2 pence, the plantation owner 10 pence, the trading company 31 pence, the ripener/distributor 17 pence and the supermarket 40 pence. It is easy to see where the money is made and, therefore, the power lies.

A key principle of market economics is the relationship between supply and demand – which determines price. With the particular dynamics of farming, this market can become distorted. When the price of a commodity goes down and farmers can no longer make a living from growing it, market theory suggests that they switch to growing another more profitable commodity. Often this is not possible due to individual land and climate suitability and the requirement to develop the necessary skills to change production to another crop as well as re-invest in new production equipment. In an attempt to maintain their income, farmers then produce even more, thus creating an oversupply. This effectively depresses the price even further, often disastrous for the farmer but not the consumer.

Historically, Ugandan coffee growers have often struggled to feed their families. Coffee prices have hovered around the cost break-even point for many years. In Uganda, however, there are few other viable crop alternatives, so coffee-growers do not exit the market, but simply

Even at the best of times, coffee farmers receive as little as 7% of the price western consumers pay for a jar of instant coffee.

redouble their efforts, adding to a global coffee surplus and further price reductions. Even at the best of times, coffee farmers receive as little as 7% of the price Western consumers pay for a jar of instant coffee. In 2001 the Brazilian government proposed the burning of over one million tonnes of coffee to restore prices to viable levels for their growers.

Capitalism's priority is the short-term profit of the farmer or company. This is inconsistent, however, with the long-term sustainability of agriculture. The logic of capitalism is straightforward: the aim is to make a profit by producing a commodity that can be sold for more than the cost of all its inputs (except the environmental ones). In seeking to maximise profits, capital will naturally gravitate towards more profitable commodities with greater margins – like highly processed cereals and snacks.

In the food production industry, businesses strive to create quarterly profits. In calculating these profits, however, the very real social, environmental and healthcare costs of production are excluded as they can be hidden or borne by the wider community or government. If these were included, the profit and loss accounts of most agricultural and food businesses would look very different. Our agricultural and food production system, increasingly organised according to these principles, has proved disastrous to both human and environmental health.

In this context, it would be irrational for a company to reduce its profits by, say, installing an expensive waste-water treatment system. The company knows that taxpayers and consumers will, in due course, pick up the bill for the increased environmental and healthcare costs associated with the company's pollution.

It has taken over 40 years for the tobacco industry to stop denying the scientific evidence that cigarettes cause lung cancer and heart disease. The industry has at last 'agreed' that smoking tobacco can, indeed, damage your health and that the habit could cause your death. In spite of these health risks, cigarettes are so profitable that they continue to be marketed and sold despite the risk of class action lawsuits by consumers or state prosecution. The tobacco industry has responded to increasingly stringent health and advertising regulations in many developed countries by turning its attention to developing economies where regulations are more lax.

131

The July 2008 scandal in China where melamine was added to baby milk preparations demonstrates just how low unscrupulous companies will stoop to make profits at the expense of consumers – even killing them.

Even in the US, where the rate of smoking has been cut by more than half, over 435,000 Americans still die every year from tobacco-related illnesses. It is estimated that tobacco companies worldwide are still attracting between 80,000 and 100,000 new smokers a day. If these smokers follow the US trends, over one billion people (80% of them in developing countries) will die of tobacco-related illnesses during the course of this century.

Now consider food consumption: a food manufacturer or service provider will produce unhealthy junk food with all its additives and chemicals if it is more profitable than producing healthy food. The same logic applies to paying the lowest possible wages to workers or farmers: the justification is that consumers benefit from lower prices. The recent July 2008 scandal in China where melamine was added to baby milk preparations demonstrates just how low unscrupulous companies will stoop to make profits at the expense of consumers – even killing them.

The focus by global food businesses on maximising short-term profits over environmental and sustainability considerations has led to deforestation, land degradation and water pollution, not to mention emptying the seas of fish. It has accelerated the clearing of forests for soy bean production in Brazil and the shift from food production to growing crops to produce ethanol fuel in the US. Ethanol production has increased the price of food for many people around the world as land is diverted away from food production, reducing supply and increasing prices.

Economic development often entails a corresponding change in diet and health. As wealth increases there is a transition from health issues such as infectious and parasitic diseases – associated with a lack of nutrition – to the chronic and degenerative diseases like heart disease, cancer and diabetes so prevalent in the First World.

Some countries like Brazil, India and, to a lesser extent China, are experiencing a First World/Third World division within their own countries. Many of their poorer citizens are undernourished while their middle classes are becoming obese. Current protests in North African and Middle Eastern countries are a clear indication that the divide between the have's and the have not's is not sustainable. The people of these countries are voting with their lives regardless of the political will and power of their ruling governments.

For the food giants, these developing countries provide huge new markets for fast food outlets, other processed foods and the fizzy drinks associated with modern Western lifestyles. Aggressive marketing helps these markets adapt rapidly to new forms of food consumption.

Our current strategy to tackle the obesity epidemic addresses the symptoms rather than identifying and remedying the underlying causes within the food system itself. Obesity rates have soared over the last 30 years. Almost 1.7 billion people are now considered to be overweight or obese, approximately 25% of the total world population. In the US almost 50% its population is overweight or obese compared to 13% in 1960. The UK is not far behind: in 2008, 25% of its population was defined as obese and 30% of all British children under 15 years old were classed as overweight.

Rising obesity rates among children worldwide may mean that they will be the first generation not to live longer than their parents. The obesity epidemic represents a time bomb in terms of healthcare costs

133

worldwide. The UK health budget in 2002 was around £68 billion and forecast to increase, at constant prices, to over £154 billion.

Rising obesity rates among children may mean that they will be the first generation not to live longer than their parents.

People across the developing world are also facing similar health problems. More than 50% of adults in Mexico, Peru, Tunisia, Brazil, Chile and Ghana are now overweight, swelling both their waistlines and the bottom lines of the multinational food companies that feed them. If we all ate just 100 calories less a day, this would cost the global food industry between US$31 and US$36 billion in annual sales.

A heavier and larger population also creates many short-term costs for society. Special ambulances to carry heavy people have recently been designed and manufactured in Britain. Hospitals now need larger beds and hoists to lift patients with weight problems onto beds. Even the funeral industry now has to offer larger coffins and wider cremation furnaces. The air transport industry has not escaped the problem, with airlines in the US being hit by additional fuel costs of an estimated US$275 million a year to carry heavier passengers.

In the US around 56,000 new packaged foods and beverages products were introduced between 2002 and 2006. Of these only 4,000 or 7% were healthy alternatives. Processing food often involves the addition of sugar, salt, fat, chemical additives, colourings and preservatives. Companies can charge more for a pre-prepared and more convenient, but often less nutritious, processed product.

Our addiction to man-made sugar additives begins in infancy. Formula-fed babies can develop a sweet tooth from feeds that contain far more sugars than breast milk. A typical formula-fed baby consumes 30,000 more calories over its first eight months of life than a breast-fed baby – the equivalent of 120 chocolate bars.

As the baby graduates to solid food, sugar additives increase. The international Codex Alimentarius Commission, established as part of the UN's FAO in 1963, sets global standards for foods. At the meeting of Codex in November 2006, the Thai government introduced a proposal to reduce the levels of sugars in baby foods from the then existing maximum of 30% to 10%, as part of the global fight against obesity. Farley's Original Rusks for babies, made by Heinz, for example, have 29 grams of sugar per 100 gram rusk: under the new proposals the sugar content would have been capped at 10 grams.

There are roughly 15 teaspoons of high-fructose corn syrup in every can of soda, and American teenagers, on average, each drink 800 cans of soda a year – or 12,000 teaspoons of sugar annually, just in their soda drinks. Sugar makes up 20% of the total calories consumed by American teenagers. With French fries representing a staggering 25% of the total US vegetable intake, it is hardly surprising that the number of overweight children in the US has tripled since 1980.

The global sugar industry, however, has enormous lobbying power and the Thai proposal was subsequently blocked by the representatives of the US and the European Union (EU). The capitalist system often allows commercial interests to prevail over those of human health. It is interesting that the US sugar industry contributed over US$3.1 million to the 2004 federal election campaign.

Our chronic diseases of affluence result from eating bad food and can be addressed only by eating better food, not through drugs and other treatments. These are just an antidote to the symptoms, and not the causes of unhealthy nutrition and overeating.

135

Over the years food and agriculture companies have grown ever larger and more powerful through mergers and acquisitions. The largest food company in the world is Nestlé and it continues to expand. Over the years Nestlé has acquired a large number of well-known brands from Rowntree (sweets), to Perrier (bottled water) and Spillers (pet foods).

Since the Second World War bigger businesses have emerged at all levels of the global food supply chain. Larger businesses are theoretically able to become more efficient through economies of scale, driving out less efficient and often smaller competitors. The replacement of small family-owned farms by larger industrialised corporate farms has occurred all over the world, and it is these corporations that have benefited from the lion's share of government farm subsidies.

The top four transnational agricultural corporations control 40% of world trade in food. The top ten agri-businesses together control half the world's supply of seed, veterinary drugs and pesticides as well as nearly a quarter of the global $3.5 trillion retail food market.

In the US food processing sector, the top four companies control over half of all beef packing, corn exports, soya bean processing, flour milling, broiler chicken and ethanol production. Between 1998 and 2004 these companies made political donations of US$104 million.

The Green Revolution exported American agricultural science and technology to many other parts of the world. Research in the US created new varieties of wheat, corn and rice with higher edible grain yields. These plants, however, need more water as well as expensive fertilisers and specialist pesticides, often produced by the very same companies which engineered the plants. In places like India this rendered farms more efficient and increased yields, but now, even decades after the Green Revolution, 233 million Indians are still undernourished.

Many smaller farmers across the world have been bypassed by the Green Revolution because they could not afford the cost of the necessary mechanisation, seeds and other inputs. Many of those who were able to get credit for these

A staggering 100,000 Punjabi farmers alone have committed suicide in the last decade.

products, often from the companies themselves, have accumulated such large debts that they have been bankrupted, with many farmers resorting to suicide. A staggering 100,000 Punjabi farmers alone have committed suicide in the last decade. Many victims, ironically, often use the same pesticides purchased for their crops to kill themselves. Indian Parliament figures suggest that an extra 16,000 suicides a year are the direct result of the introduction of GM crops.

The next biotechnological Green Revolution will probably be structured along the same lines. As crops are re-engineered to be more water- and salt-resistant there will be huge potential profits to US biotechnology giants. At the same time this will perpetuate rural dependency and overborrowing, contributing to more suicides among smaller farmers.

The increase of meat in our diets is straining our land's capacity to produce grain and soya for feed. The FAO forecasts that total global meat consumption will almost double from 240 million tonnes in 2010 to 465 million tonnes by 2050. This will require the production of an additional one billion tonnes of animal feed. Most of this extra demand for meat will come from the rising middle class in developing countries.

Animals concentrate and transform land- and marine-based protein from plants and fishmeal into meat and farmed fish for human consumption. Already over a third of the global annual grain output of two billion tonnes is fed to farmed animals as is over one-third of all the fish caught at sea.

137

Americans are the world's leading meat-eaters, each consuming 100 kilograms a year. If everyone ate this amount of meat, the global grain production could support only 2.6 billion people – less than 40% of our current population. In order to support a future 9.2 billion people at current levels of grain production and without severe food shortages a significant change would be needed. Humans would be able to eat, on average, only 5.5 kilograms of meat a year, the current meat consumption figure in India. Indians consume 90% of their grain directly. We may have experience of feeding an extra 70 million mouths a year, but now we have three billion people all wanting to move up the food chain at the same time.

Most of the world's productive land is already in agricultural use. The conversion of land to industrial and urban use means that 80% of the extra grain required by 2030 will have to come from intensification of production on existing land. Consequently, average existing yields will need to rise from 1.1 tonnes to 1.5 tonnes per acre, a tough challenge. Average yields are increasing much more slowly than they were 30 years ago and the increase is not keeping up with growth in demand. In some areas where the soil is not healthy – or overused – yields are falling.

At the same time as man has urbanised, so we have urbanised our domestic livestock. A dairy farm of 40,000 cows, a beef farm of 100,000 cattle, a chicken farm producing one million chickens a day – these are industrial animals cities, designed to feed human ones.

Applying technology and industrial production processes to meat production has led to the development of what are termed Concentrated Animal Feeding Operations (CAFOs). CAFOs already account for over 40% of global meat production. Traditionally, livestock farms have allowed cattle space to graze and time to grow, but the development of grain feeding allowed meat production to become an industrial process.

Animal rations are calculated by feed management software in order to ensure the quickest weight gain for the lowest nutritional input cost. This means that a six-month-old 250 kilogram feeder calf can be fattened up to over 600 kilograms in a mere four months. The same calf naturally fed on grass would take two years to reach a similar weight.

The meat from grain-fed feedlots has a much higher level of saturated fat than that of natural grass-fed animals. Grass-fed animals are leaner and their meat contains much higher levels of polyunsaturated fats which are known to be healthier than saturated fats and therefore reduce the risk from meat consumption of heart disease and other illnesses: the health choice is clear.

CAFOs often treat animals as industrial inputs to be reared, fattened and slaughtered. Producing the maximum edible yield in the minimum possible time is often the only way to stay in business, with little regard for animal welfare, product flavour or consumer health. This intensive production involves the extensive use of antibiotics, growth hormones, selective breeding and, for example with salmon, genetic modification. Humans, in turn, absorb these stimulants, which may go some way to explaining the worldwide phenomenon of earlier human puberty.

In milk production, a grass-fed cow can naturally produce around 25 litres a day, but this is boosted to over 50 litres with grain-fed diets. This means that the cow cannot be allowed to graze outside if she is to reach the target milk yield. Cows subjected to this regime are more susceptible to disease and do not live as long as their grass-fed counterparts.

Many intensive production facilities fail to meet the recognised minimum criteria for animal welfare, including freedom from discomfort and the freedom to express normal behaviour. Cows are separated from their calves shortly after birth and fed vast quantities

139

of food to increase and maintain their milk yields. It is not surprising that less than half of the cows subjected to such conditions last more than three lactations.

We need to address the way we treat animals in factory farms. For most people it is a case of out of sight, out of mind and meat simply appears on the plate via the supermarket. These ethical animal treatment issues do not come up except where activists attempt to ban particularly inhumane farming practices. They have recently targeted production methods – such as the use of veal crates and sow stalls – which restrict the animals' movement to improve output.

Competition in the animal production industry has led to giant, integrated factory operations with their attendant economies of scale, but also an industrial sale of waste production. The amount of concentrated waste generated by CAFOs and not returned to the land for natural recycling is largely ignored. A typical pig produces three gallons of faeces and urine every day; a farm with 5,000 pigs will produce as much manure as a town of 20,000 people. This cocktail of potentially toxic pollutants is not recycled, but is often stored, instead, in huge lagoons. These are cost centres not profit generators, and are therefore prone to a lack of maintenance and leaks.

US feedlots produce around 300 million tonnes of waste a year. The run-off, as from piggeries, often ends up in rivers and therefore eventually in the seas. This pollution contributes to the creation of dead zones around estuaries killing our marine fish. Like nuclear power plants, CAFOs are potentially hazardous facilities, but because they are agricultural facilities they are largely exempt from environmental regulations.

Of all these intensive operations, those raising beef are the most grain intensive. It takes on average 24 kilograms of grain to produce one kilogram of beef and seven kilograms of grain to produce a kilogram of pork.

The FAO estimates that up to 18% of all greenhouse gas emissions are due to livestock farming. Their forecast of increased demand for meat will produce a corresponding increase in these emissions. Animals like fish and chickens with one stomach (mono-gastric) require a higher protein diet than ruminants (for example: cows with their multiple stomachs). Animal protein is a natural part of the diet of mono-gastric animals.

Mono-gastric animals consume a great deal of protein rich soya. The primary growing region for soya is Brazil, and as demand for soya increases, there will be further deforestation to create more arable land for planting soya crops. A fifth of the Amazon rainforest has already been cleared, and 80% of this was initially appropriated for cattle ranching on what was virgin land. More than 20% of these ranches have subsequently been converted to soya production. Brazil exports soya mainly to China and the EU, where 90% of it is consumed by farmed animals.

Intensive chicken production began in earnest in the 1930s and now these factories are responsible for 75% of world production. Chickens for meat production are selectively bred and industrially farmed. As with livestock, the trend has been towards large, mechanised poultry farms. With computer-controlled process automation, just two people can manage the production of up to 250,000 birds at a time. Their life cycle is sped up using all the technology available to the factory in order to shorten the time taken to reach target slaughter weight.

It takes on average 24 kilograms of grain to produce one kilogram of beef and seven kilograms of grain to produce a kilogram of pork.

Industrially farmed chickens are bred to convert their feed into breast meat. Most chicken meat is now sold as fillets and cuts, as opposed

141

to whole birds, with the most valuable part being the breast portions. This selective breeding has advanced to the point where the chickens' breasts have grown so large that their legs often cannot support their bodies and many can hardly stand on their feet.

In the 1970s a chicken took ten weeks to reach 1.5 kilograms, while today's birds reach 2.2 kilograms in half that time. From hatching, most birds are supermarket-ready in less than 40 days. It's all about the performance of the chicken in terms of its Feed Conversion Ratio (FCR). The most efficient producers use 2.6 kilograms of feed to produce one kilogram of chicken. Since we eat only part of the bird, the real conversion rate is nearer 4.5 kilograms of grain to make the one kilogram of chicken meat that we will actually eat. It takes as much energy, food and water to make the bits we don't eat as the bits that we do eat.

The annual slaughter of chickens produces 10 billion litres of blood, the equivalent of nearly 400,000 petrol tankers.

Over 50 billion chickens are reared annually, and there are 16 billion chickens alive at any one time. The slaughter of these chickens produces 10 billion litres of blood, the equivalent of nearly 400,000 petrol tankers. Much of this is poured into ponds and left to seep into the ground.

The poultry industry provides a good example of intense competition cutting margins to the bone. Large grocery chains and fast food companies can exert enormous pressure on suppliers, whose profit margin can be under five US cents per kilogram of chicken. Producers are locked into a system where they are continually obliged to strive for further economies of scale, often at the expense of the animals' welfare and the environment.

This has encouraged even more finely tuned feed ration management and the maximum possible automation of the breeding and slaughter process. Whereas 30 years ago the largest processing plants handled only 16 million birds a year, a large modern operation may produce up to 250 million chickens a year.

Over the last 30 years, US chicken production has tripled yet the meat price has plummeted in real terms to only a quarter of what it was in 1980. This is good news for consumers, but not for those working in the industry whose wages declined by 24% over the same period. With profit margins reduced to the bare minimum, food processors are often obliged to seek out regions or countries with lower regulatory environments, or alternatively to merge into ever-larger scale conglomerates.

Intense animal production increases the danger of infectious disease transmission. Since industrially farmed animals are genetically selected for maximum yield, there are fewer genetic strains. They are effectively a monoculture as they are all so alike. This selection process drains their genetic vitality and compromises their natural immune system. To keep them healthy they are fed huge doses of antibiotics often as a preventative measure rather than as a treatment for an illness.

This overuse of antibiotics can lead to drug-resistant bacteria developing. We have seen outbreaks of so called superbugs in hospitals as they become resistant to anti-bacterial solutions. The recent outbreak in India of a waterborne, drug-resistant bacteria NDM-1 gene makes bacteria resistant to a large range of antibiotics. The same happens in our animal factories: we now need ever-stronger antibiotics to kill off disease and maintain food production.

The livestock industry today consumes almost half of all antibiotics produced in the world. The doses used in poultry production have tripled over the last 30 years, making it more likely that bacteria will evolve and develop into drug-resistant forms that could potentially unleash epidemics in animal as well as in human populations.

143

Cows naturally eat grass, but slaughterhouse waste – including blood, offal, excrement and other protein sources – has been used in industrial feed as a protein supplement. Although banned in the UK in 1988, its use continued for some years. First discovered in 1986, a massive outbreak of Bovine Spongiform Encephalopathy (BSE) occurred in cattle in the early 1990s. Its human form Creutzfeldt-Jakob disease (CJD) appeared some years later in 1996. These specific disease strains were the direct result of competitive pressures on producers. Slaughterhouse by-products may be cheaper than other protein sources, but bending the rules of Nature has its consequences.

While suffering some short-term loss, the agri-industry did not pay the full costs of the BSE outbreak. The cost of the wholesale slaughtering of cows and the expenses of human health were covered by the UK taxpayer. With this separation of cause and financial consequence the industry is unlikely to act voluntarily to prevent future disasters.

Some diseases can be transmitted from animals to humans. These include bird and swine flu. Although wild birds have been blamed for the recent emergence of H5N1, it is more likely that these disease strains have emerged from establishing production sites for millions of chickens alongside commercial piggeries. The proximity of these intensive but different farming operations provides ideal conditions for bacteria and viruses to mutate into evermore deadly forms.

Recent swine and avian flu outbreaks may come to be seen as benign compared to animal and human diseases that will naturally evolve in time to come.

The H1N1 swine flu virus originates from a triple hybrid human/pig/bird flu virus that emerged and spread throughout factory farms in US more than a decade ago and into humans in 2009 in Veracruz, Mexico. Flu viruses generally kill between 250,000 and 500,000 people per year. This swine flu outbreak was not as virulent as first thought and killed a relatively small number of people – some 18,000 during the year to March 2011.

Such outbreaks have now, however, flagged the potential of intensive farming operations to foster such new diseases. Recent swine and avian flu outbreaks may come to be seen as benign compared to animal and human diseases that will naturally evolve in time to come. We urgently need to reconsider the effects and implications of intensive livestock production. It has consequences not only for the animals themselves, but the system also poses dangers to human health.

Public health organisations have a vital role to play in regulating food production systems. Public health can either focus on the population as a whole by, for example, banning certain foods or additives, or on individual choice, for example, in allowing tobacco smoking despite its known health risks. The food industry favours the individual approach, with the onus squarely on the consumer.

Processed food producers stress that consumers are personally responsible for any consequences that might arise from eating their products. Even light or healthy products often carry the warning that they are to be consumed only as part of a calorie-controlled diet. Even with this focus on personal responsibility, it is the population as a whole that picks up the costs of any consequences.

The US food industry lobbied strongly for the Personal Responsibility in Food Consumption Act, passed by the US Congress in 2004. Despite this, and their new emphasis on balanced diet and exercise, a Class Action lawsuit was launched against the fast food companies in New York in July 2010. As with tobacco companies this will be a long and drawn-out process. Unlike smoking, however, we all need to eat.

145

Health policymakers in the UK and in other developed countries have already started advocating a reduction in meat consumption. Overall, wealthy societies need to reduce their consumption of meat and dairy products. In tandem, developing countries must be encouraged to curb their aspirations to eat more of these food types. Culturally and socially, this is an extraordinarily challenging agenda since higher meat and dairy consumption is perceived as a symbol of economic and social progress.

We need a new vision for public health that considers the close interrelationship between environmental and human health. Good nutrition is fundamental to human health, while sustainable agricultural practices are surely fundamental to environmental health: the two are deeply interconnected systems. A merging by the UN of the FAO and the WHO would send a strong and meaningful message to national structures all over the world.

With the FAO projecting a near-doubling of meat consumption by 2050, this can only mean a further increase in the scale and intensity of the factory farming of animals. This is, however, unsustainable and unacceptable on both ecological and animal welfare grounds.

CAFOs must be legally obliged to provide more humane conditions for rearing their animals and to recycle their waste. Developed countries must also stop subsidising those farmers and businesses that follow environmentally poor farming practices. We must, conversely, start taxing these organisations with the actual cost of their environmental impact or at least some of the risk cost. You, as a consumer, can also play a role in supporting primary producers in developing countries, by supporting initiatives such as 'Fair Trade' products.

You, as a consumer, can also play a role in supporting primary producers in developing countries by supporting 'Fair Trade' products.

The impact on human and environmental health of modern industrial agriculture is the result of failures in the free market system, not in agriculture itself. This international market has been tampered with by national subsidies to farmers in wealthy countries distorting trade. A lack of government foresight in its regulatory environment further distorts the market and promotes waste, through, for example, mandating the size and appearance of fresh produce.

Minimum international standards on all aspects of industrial farming should be agreed and implemented, so that no single country finds itself at a competitive disadvantage by complying with such necessary regulation. We need an international code of best practice which protects the interests of producers and consumers.

This means finding new ways of strengthening democracy and making corporations and markets more transparent in their operations and more directly accountable for their actions. However, what is currently politically feasible under our capitalist democracy falls well short of what is ecologically necessary to save our planet.

CHAPTER SIX – **LESS MEETS MORE: THE PROTEIN CRUNCH**

We get all our food from two sources – the land and the seas. When we talk about food what we really mean is protein, whether plant-based or animal-based. The ecosystems that provide these food sources are being rapidly degraded, and their capacity to produce, even at current levels, is in doubt.

As we add more and more people to our planet every day we have more and more demand for protein, yet the natural resources with which to create it are finite. When more meets less, we face what we call the Protein Crunch. Our changing climate will bring forward the onset and increase the severity of the Protein Crunch. The last decade has been the warmest in history, with 2005 and 2010 the hottest since records began. It does not matter if this temperature increase is man-made or just a natural cycle – the climate is without question changing. Nineteen countries experienced record temperatures in 2010. The July temperature in Moscow was 14 degrees Fahrenheit above average, and more than 300 fires started every day in the surrounding countryside. More than 56,000 people died in the extreme heat, 3,000 more than in the European heat wave of 2003.

A team at the US-based National Center for Atmospheric Research has found that the surface area of the Earth subject to very dry conditions, expanded from less than 15% in the 1970s to around 30% by 2002. Current warming trends will only make this worse.

Crop ecologists calculate that each one degree Celsius rise in temperature above the optimum during the growing season produces a 10% decline in grain yields. In Russia during its 2010 heat wave, the annual harvest fell from 100 million to 60 million tonnes.

Warming weather patterns are melting our polar ice sheets and mountain snow caps. Even a moderate resulting rise in sea levels of less than a metre would flood many rice-growing areas in countries

149

such as Bangladesh and Vietnam, as well as fertile estuaries and other low-lying croplands around the world.

2010 saw a dramatic worsening of the global agricultural situation. There were severe droughts in China, India, Canada and Russia, reducing their grain outputs. Grain stockpiles have fallen to record lows. Russia even banned grain exports to keep domestic prices down.

In 2010 and 2011 Pakistan and Australia suffered some of the worst floods in living memory, and farmers there are now trying to adapt to and mitigate the effects of climate change on their agricultural production. Further yield-reducing weather patterns will destabilise the world food economy, putting pressure on commodity and food prices.

Already in early 2011, the FAO is warning of the implications of a severe winter drought for wheat production in the North China Plain. There has been very little rain since October 2010, which has affected the snow cover required to protect the plants against frost damage as well as levels of moisture in the soil needed when growth resumes. The fertile North China Plain accounts for two-thirds of China's national crop.

Chinese government estimates suggest that more than 5 million out of 14 million hectares have been affected by the drought, directly impacting not only 2.5 million people but also 2.8 million livestock that don't have enough water to drink. This will put further pressure on international wheat prices, which have already reached record levels in 2011.

Food price increases are currently running well ahead of the general inflation rate. India, for instance, is currently struggling with an 18% annual food price inflation rate. The FAO food price index reached record levels in December 2010 and rose a further 3% in January 2011.

If prices continue to rise, we will be in uncharted territory in terms of political instability. We may see more riots and unrest, even beyond what we have already seen in 2008 and early 2011. The immediate stability of world food prices now depends on there being a bumper grain harvest like that of 2008. We consumed 60 million tonnes of grain more than we produced in 2010, and demand will increase by a further 40 million tonnes in 2011. So we need an extra 100 million tonnes to make up the shortfall – but this looks unlikely to happen with droughts in China and the US.

Many of the countries with the fastest-growing populations in the world were severely impacted by the 2008 food crisis and appear on the Fund for Peace list of failing states, including Somalia, Sudan, Zimbabwe, Afghanistan and Iraq. These countries are the most vulnerable to internal violence and social disintegration. The number of failing and failed states is expected to increase as the Protein Crunch bites.

Pressure on commodity prices is coming from reduced supply as well as increased demand from a growing population. Then there is the added effect of using more than a quarter of the US grain crop to produce ethanol for cars – enough grain to feed 350 million people. A typical SUV fill-up at the petrol station uses the same amount of grain as would feed one person for a year. Cars are now competing with people (and animals) for the world grain harvest. Fuel for the cars of the rich is taking food from the mouths of the poor.

A typical SUV fill-up at the petrol station uses the same amount of grain as would feed one person for a year. Cars are now competing with people (and animals) for the world grain harvest. Fuel for the cars of the rich is taking food from the mouths of the poor.

We have seen how we are facing a potential global crisis of food supply: the Protein Crunch. Forecasts indicate that we need to grow 50% more food by 2030 and double the amount we currently grow by 2050 to meet our changing

151

patterns of consumption and growing population. Yet the amount of available land and water is decreasing, as is the renewable output of our seas. So we can foresee a Protein Crunch even if we cannot predict precisely when it will happen.

We are already operating beyond the Earth's renewable carrying capacity, and have been doing so since the mid-1990s. We are currently consuming more than 135% of renewable planetary resources. According to the Global Footprint Network (GFN), an international think-tank offering assistance in measuring environmental impacts, we continue to overuse our renewable resources on a global scale. The day in the annual calendar by which we have used the year's renewable resources is termed 'Earth Overshoot Day'. This is the date by which we are overdrawn on Nature's current account and begin to mortgage on our future. In 2007 this was 19 October, in 2008 it was 23 September and by 2010 it arrived on 21 August. This current 35% overshoot will rise to nearly 100% by 2050, when we will need almost two Earths to support us sustainably.

Politicians find themselves in a real dilemma. On the one hand, economic growth can't continue indefinitely in its current form – since 1950 we have consumed half the resources ever used. On the other hand, we can't stop growth without creating recession and unemployment, and civil unrest, as we have increasingly seen since 2008.

All the major governmental reviews, like the UK's recent Future of Food and Farming Report, agree that the case for urgent action in the global food system is now compelling. They argue that we are at a unique moment in history when various factors are converging to affect the demand, production and distribution of food over the next 20 to 30 years.

We think the Protein Crunch will arrive much sooner. We have seen how critical resources such as water, energy and land are becoming increasingly stretched, and how the current system can't even feed the existing population adequately, let alone another two billion people.

The Ministries of Agriculture in both Italy and the UK have said that our food systems must become sustainable – a tacit admission that they currently are not. Food production already dominates much of our landscape, and without radical change, the global food system will continue to degrade the environment. This will limit our capacity to produce food in the future, contribute to further climate change and the destruction of biodiversity. Agriculture, conversely, needs to make a substantial contribution to climate change mitigation and repairing the environment.

The Protein Crunch is happening as we write. The price rises of 2008 and 2010 are the tangible effect of the markets managing the imbalance between supply and demand in our rapidly changing food supply systems. Often the notions of environmental impact that we have been discussing seem distant and unlikely to affect us as individuals. This is already not the case: we are being affected today, although many of us do not yet realise it.

Wealthier individuals spend a smaller proportion of their income on food than poorer people. In countries like Tunisia, Algeria and Egypt, many people spend more than 50% of their income on food. In other parts of Africa the poor spend as much as 80% of their income on food. Food price inflation hits the poor particularly hard. A near-40% spike in food prices in 2008 caused food riots around the world as far afield as Morocco, Yemen, Mexico, Guinea, Mauritania, Senegal and Uzbekistan.

In January 2008 Pakistan was forced to reintroduce rationing for the first time in 20 years. Russia froze the price of milk, bread, eggs and cooking oil for six months and other countries like Thailand and

Indonesia implemented a freeze on food staples or increased public food subsidies. India banned the export of its rice, except the high-quality basmati variety. The Mexican government purchased corn futures to avoid a sharp rise in the price of tortillas. All these efforts were attempts to reduce civil unrest in their countries caused by food price rises.

In April of the same year, the government of Haiti was toppled as a result of several weeks of rioting over food prices. Food prices and hunger were the tipping points for the recent 2010 unrest in the Middle East. Other countries that have recently seen food riots include Morocco, Jordan, Mozambique and Chile. Food price protests driven by frustration have occurred in Italy and Greece, and these may in future become food riots driven by hunger.

Fossil fuels are key inputs in fertiliser production, as well as in powering agricultural machinery and the transport of food. So higher oil and gas prices bring more food unrest, and with it violence onto our streets and political instability that drives commodity prices higher still, in a vicious circle.

US Secretary of State Hillary Clinton in March 2011 warned that rising food prices are a threat to global growth and social stability. Robert Zoellick, president of the World Bank, also warned that with falling grain stocks we are just one poor harvest or environmental disaster away from chaos.

We need to redouble our efforts to address hunger, which continues to affect so many people. Much of this hunger is a direct result of how the global capitalist food system operates. We need to help the poor and hungry, not just out of charity but because their plight will increasingly affect us directly.

In terms of security, we still put the main emphasis on military security without realising that food and environmental security are in fact far more critical. We cannot eat arms. We have already seen how food insecurity leads to political instability.

A further security challenge will be the rising tide of environmental refugees, defined by the UN as people displaced due to environmental causes. These might be gradual environmental shifts like land loss and degradation, or a sudden, man-made environmental disaster like the floods in Pakistan. The UN estimates that there are up to 50 million environmental refugees worldwide, more than those displaced by war and political repression combined. Environmental refugees are already streaming from North Africa to Europe. Unless we address the root causes, however, this movement of people from one area to another may be akin to rearranging the deck chairs on the *Titanic*.

Failing states will drive a wave of hungry environmental refugees who may strip the fields in the poorer regions on which the rich depend for their food. Half of the peas and beans in Europe are grown in Kenya. Saudi Arabia's wheat comes from starving Sudan and its fruit from South Africa. Should this crop theft happen on a large scale, then agricultural collapse is more likely, as farmers will be reluctant to replant for the following season. Already stock theft, particularly of sheep, from farms both in the UK and South Africa is rapidly increasing. This causes farmers either to reduce their herds or to leave the market altogether.

Nothing less than a redesign of the whole food system along sustainable principles is required.

Nothing less than a redesign of the whole food system along sustainable principles is required. In this sense, the recent demise of the UK Sustainable Development Commission is a short-sighted move when sustainability needs to be embedded across and between government departments.

There is no alternative to what is being called `sustainable intensification' because there is relatively little new land for agriculture at a time when more food needs to be produced. Sustainable intensification involves raising yields at the same time as increasing the efficiency with which inputs and irrigation are used.

Ignoring the symptoms of the Protein Crunch is becoming less possible by the day, as newspaper reports of protests and dissent over food prices increase. What is missing is the understanding of the underlying cause of the price rises – our environmental degradation combined with a daily increasing population. In the last chapter we will explore what we should be doing to address these issues.

CHAPTER SEVEN – **CHALLENGES AND CHOICES**

The year 2012 marks a number of anniversaries: 50 years since the publication of Rachel Carson's *Silent Spring;* 40 years since the United Nations (UN) Stockholm Conference on the Environment; 20 years since the UN's sustainable development action plan, *Agenda 21,* was agreed at the Rio de Janeiro Earth Summit, and 10 years since the Johannesburg Summit on Sustainable Development and the formulation of the Earth Charter.

In 1992 the Union of Concerned Scientists Warning to Humanity was published and signed by 1,700 scientists, including most of the scientific Nobel Laureates at that time. Most official and authoritative publications on the environment since then are sending out the same signal: humanity is on a collision course with Nature.

Recent studies of our reactions to environmental issues suggest that the more informed we are about our ecological prospects, the more pessimistic we become. We cannot just continue with 'business as usual'. We are already past the point of our sustainable use of the environment and heading for eventual environmental meltdown. The problem with using resources in an unsustainable manner is that no one really believes in unsustainability until there is nothing left or the system is demonstrably broken. We have been using the Earth's resources unsustainably for many decades, and as a consequence we have a limited time to react, act and make a meaningful and sustainable difference. If we don't act, Nature will – in the form of unexpected crises and system collapses. Nature is rather like a goose laying golden eggs. When egg production stops we want goose feather pillows, then *foie gras,* and then roast goose sandwiches every day until there's nothing left: then we will want our goose back.

The pressure on our natural resources such as water, soil, forests, the oceans and biodiversity has continued relentlessly. The environmental damage already inflicted by industrial agriculture, aquifer depletion, overfishing, deforestation, species loss, and climate change is huge.

Scientists warn that our tampering with the world's interdependent web of life could trigger widespread adverse effects. These could include unpredictable crises arising from interactions between climate and forests, water and food, intensive feedlots and disease pandemics.

When it comes to national security, we don't hesitate to apply the precautionary principle, working out the worst-case scenarios and designing defence policies to address these possibilities. We haven't yet done this for environmental security. We are only just beginning to realise the extent of our ecological and food security challenges and the ways in which they impact on political stability and regional security. By creating a food security budget we could, correspondingly, reduce military expenditure.

Humans have had extensive experience over thousands of years of reacting to immediate danger. If we see a dangerous wild animal or a car heading towards us, we react quickly. The brain goes into fight or flight mode, and we mobilise the necessary resources for immediate action. Unfortunately we tend to ignore the stimuli we receive alerting us to the danger of a long-term or seemingly distant emergency like that of environmental degradation. Our individual – and therefore collective – response is too slow with the result that we don't realise the need to react until it's almost too late – if we react at all.

Smog resulting from household coal fires had been accumulating over London since the late 1800s, causing widespread respiratory disease. However, it was not until the great four-day smog in 1952 had killed over 4,000 people that the British government reacted and introduced air pollution control measures. How many lives and how much misery might have been saved with more timely action? Hindsight, we know, does not help.

None of the ecological crises we have faced so far has been severe enough to galvanise our efforts on a global scale. Besides, there are always sceptics to reassure us that a particular crisis is not in fact connected to other environmental events or issues we see around us, and we therefore carry on regardless.

Perhaps the world needs a visible and tangible environmental mega-crisis to achieve a coordinated and committed response to global environmental degradation. This need for a disaster may sound pessimistic, but it is hard to envisage how else we will find the resolve to change as quickly as we need to. Humans make changes for two reasons: inspiration or desperation. Many of us can't bring ourselves to change those habits or lifestyles that we know are harmful to us until they threaten our very existence.

We spend trillions of dollars on human healthcare and invest almost nothing in caring for the Earth on which we all depend. The only good news is that we will live long enough to see how stupid we were.

For some, the 'wake-up call' can be a near-death experience. Are we heading for a planetary near-death experience before we wake up to what we need to do? We are ignoring the warnings of informed scientists and passionate individuals as 'inconvenient truths'. We should be concerned about the futures of our children and grandchildren. They will live with the consequences of our current decisions and actions. We spend trillions of dollars on human healthcare and invest almost nothing in caring for the Earth on which we all depend. The only good news is that we will live long enough to see how stupid we were.

Worse still is that the global environmental degradation we are currently causing is avoidable. We can make a difference: we have the knowledge, ability and technology. What we lack right now is the will, leadership and commitment.

161

The author of *Small is Beautiful,* EF Schumacher, said that he didn't mind being called a crank as a crank was, in fact, a useful tool that performed revolutions. Revolutions, however, are disturbing. A British civil servant, when asked what kind of change he favoured and when he'd like it to happen, is said to have responded: "gradual, and in due course". This dictate won't be good enough to save our human civilisation as we know it. Many people, including His Royal Highness the Prince of Wales in his recent book *Harmony – A New Way of Looking at the World,* argue for a sustainability revolution.

Over the last centuries, our particular thinking and values have created our current economic systems and political institutions. Given our changed environmental circumstances, many are no longer fit for purpose. Since we created them, we surely have the capacity to change them. Once enough of us realise the issues we are facing, we will reach a point of common consciousness. This will allow us to update our international institutions and systems to deliver the change we need.

The pace of change in the world is accelerating and tipping points, like the recent events in Tunisia and across the Middle East, cause rapid and widespread change. We may yet get our sustainability revolution more quickly than we think.

Our current international institutions were set up to manage our then common interests. The United Nations and its core agencies including the Food and Agriculture Organisation, the International Maritime Organisation, the World Bank and the International Monetary Fund addressed the key issues at the time of their creation. These UN agencies, while having a global remit, are subject to the power of national politics. Individual UN member countries continue to set the UN's agenda and pursue their own short-term interests at the expense of the long-term interests of the planet. Our new institutions, like many central banks, need a clear mandate and independence from their political masters.

The thinking behind a sustainability revolution must to be based on two fundamental assumptions and two corresponding ethical imperatives: the assumptions are that the long-term health and the interests of the whole planet must come before those of individual nation states or blocs, and that our economic systems in the future must be repositioned and be subservient to ecological systems instead of the other way round. Ethically, this means that we must begin to consider and act in the long-term interests of the whole planet and that we must create a viable global eco-economy, working in harmony with Nature to sustain natural systems.

We need to harness the energy and capital of entrepreneurs and businesses to deliver this and also change our definitions of success. This requires designing new measures of well-being and progress such as Gross National Happiness (GNH) or the Genuine Progress Indicator (GPI) – beyond just the economic consumption indicator of Gross Domestic Product (GDP).

It is important to distinguish between growth and development. It has often been assumed that economic growth leads to happiness, but research shows that this is only partly true. Beyond a comfortable level of income, people don't actually become any happier, but development in a personal sense – through, for example, learning new skills – becomes more important. We don't grow physically past our 20s – but there is no limit to our intellectual and personal development.

Our new thinking processes need to be based on Nature rather than technology. We need to begin to understand the complex web of life rather than tinker with the parts of an imaginary machine that we consider Nature.

Our new thinking processes need to be based on Nature rather than technology. We need to begin to understand the complex web of

163

life rather than tinker with the parts of an imaginary machine that we consider Nature.

W hen we eat or drink, our body sends us feedback signals when we are full, so we stop. Feedback from Nature does not always come to us directly – Nature often responds where we least expect a reaction. EU citizens buy subsidised fish caught off West Africa by European trawlers that have put local fishermen out of business and reduced them to the breadline. These fishermen then become economic or environmental migrants to Europe.

Nature has yet to speak to us loudly enough in terms of a 'minimum necessary catastrophe' to make us all pay attention.

Our delayed, diluted or dispersed feedback provides no impetus to act. Nature has yet to speak to us loudly enough in terms of a 'minimum necessary catastrophe' to make us all pay attention.

When we are faced with the reality of an ecological crisis – or an impending crisis – we are generally responding or reacting in five different ways. First, there are the loners who remove themselves from the system altogether. They are often survivalist in nature and do not see the environment as their issue. The pessimists or fatalists believe nothing can be done to change things, some even think that nothing should be done. Many Christian fundamentalists in the United States welcome the onset of this environmental mayhem as the 'beginning of the end' as prophesied in the Bible. Others anticipate the end of the world in 2012 according to the Mayan calendar and are therefore not interested in long-term issues.

Then there are three kinds of people who adopt a more active role and engage with the challenges we face. Each thinks about the issues and looks for solutions in different ways. They can be categorised as individualists, egalitarians and hierocrats.

Individualists are optimists who believe in human ingenuity and Nature's resilience. They think that technology and free markets can fix any problem we may have and that nothing should get in the way of the globalisation of freedom and GDP-based prosperity. They believe that human history has shown that we can master Nature through the brilliance of our minds and inventiveness of our technology. The events of the last century have given these individualist thinkers cause to confirm their beliefs, as the human world has risen to many of the challenges presented to it by Nature.

Egalitarians are more pessimistic and 'green' by nature. They think that the environment needs protection from further human exploitation and that our planetary life-support systems are endangered. They encourage a transition to a more benign, self-sufficient, localised and environmentally sustainable lifestyle. They argue that technical fixes are inadequate while a dysfunctional economic and political system remains in place. They believe that the inequalities in the world created by these systems need to be addressed as a part of the environmental solution. The human future to these egalitarian thinkers means more people, more consumption and more disruption of natural systems. They want to find a way of stopping this by putting on the emergency brake.

Lastly the hierocrat thinks in terms of plans, policies, stewardship and appropriate regulations to move civilisation forward. The hierocrat believes that institutions like the UN and capitalist free-market democracy have served us well so far, and it will suffice to continually update the mandates of these institutions. He would argue for more developmental policies and practices and the setting of international development frameworks, trusting in the system, albeit an updated one, to deliver the necessary change.

The critical tension here is between individualists and egalitarians, between generally right-wing technological optimists who tend to be sceptical environmentalists, and generally left-wing ecological pessimists who think that technological optimists are living on borrowed time with a profit agenda. By the same token, individualists regard egalitarians as naysayers, purveyors of a doomsday scenario that has not happened as forecast and probably won't.

We must harness all these action-orientated thinkers and use the strengths of the capitalist system to encourage them to address the challenges of the environment. We need to be innovative in finding sustainable solutions to our challenges and simultaneously create a global governance framework within which we can manage our creativity and conservation actions.

We live in an age of 'supercapitalism', the result of increasingly intense competition between businesses for both investors and customers. In this context we as individuals play three roles: investor, consumer and citizen. Competition between companies in the food supply chain has resulted in a huge consolidation of power within this business sector. Business power then merges with politics through lobbying activity and campaign contributions.

So governments are beholden to big business as much as to citizens. Such is the clout of multinational corporations around the world that the power of democracy becomes compromised. It is these businesses, however, that have been driving deregulation of markets, including that of the financial markets, which led to the 2008 credit crunch.

Competition in business has led to lower prices for us as consumers, and better returns as investors. It has, however, compromised our role as citizens to whom governments should be accountable for managing our long-term futures.

As citizens, we must recover our voice and our capacity to hold governments accountable and oriented towards the common good.

As citizens, we must recover our voice and our capacity to hold governments accountable and oriented towards the common good. This will involve legislation to limit political contributions and bring in more public finance for election campaigns.

The Internet provides a superb new avenue for the expression of citizen concern. Online petitions can attract hundreds of thousands of signatures in days. Many of the campaigns at Avaaz and Care2 have involved ecological issues - supporting them sends an increasingly loud message to decision makers, captains of industry, lobbyists, publicity agents, politicians, civil servants, and – not forgetting – prime ministers and presidents.

Consumers like us have increasing power to influence large companies through value-driven purchases. Fair Trade products are rapidly increasing their market penetration, and new websites like GoodGuide and Earthster provide consumers with an ecological life cycle assessment (LCA) of the goods they buy. An LCA covers the whole range of impacts from 'cradle to grave' and allows people to make choices based on the same kind of sustainability information that the company itself has – or at least should have.

This 'radical transparency' of full information about products can link business ethics to the bottom line. The primary focus of companies is to maximise shareholder value, but in order to do this they need to retain their customers. If these customers are demanding sustainable products, then the company that best satisfies these demands will make the most money. This means that informed consumers have the power to change company behaviour.

We are often urged to think globally and act locally, but the reality of government and international agreements is that we postpone agreed and long-overdue initiatives while other countries are doing

167

the same for fear of putting themselves at a first-mover economic disadvantage. The wording of sustainable development action plans such as the UN's *Agenda 21* is the result of horse-trading and compromise in an attempt to reach a consensus wording and reconcile competing interests. Oil-producing nations like Saudi Arabia and Kuwait, for instance, watered down passages in the Agenda promoting solar energy. In the same way, the US blocked any reference to the Earth Charter from the final Political Declaration at Johannesburg in 2002. This omission will have been used as a bargaining chip by other governments who wanted to include wording that protected their perceived interests.

Such conferences and declarations have produced noteworthy aspirations reported in the media, but the hopes and expectations raised have so far not been met, as there has been a lack of political will to deliver. This has been true of every major meeting in the last 40 years. There is a marked tension between the urgency of scientific pronouncements and the sluggishness of political processes. Politicians are geared to mobilise rapidly only in times of war.

We can see in failing and failed states around the world a microcosm of what our world could look like if we do not act. Failing states are to some extent contagious within a region as migration, political turmoil and environmental degradation often burden neighbouring states. The drivers of their collapse are cumulative environmental damage, climate change and business and food insecurity. Food insecurity has – and will again – lead to food riots and cause political instability. This unrest will not be confined to the developing world; there have already been food price protests in Greece and Italy in 2008. In March 2011 a senior economist at the worldwide bank HSBC warned of civil unrest in Britain if food prices continue to soar.

Environmental crises are not new and have hit many earlier civilisations. The collapse of the early Mesoamerican, Mayan, Easter Islander and Roman civilisations have environmental damage at their core. The traditional human response to such environmental crises has been conflict, social breakdown, civil and intertribal (now international) resource conflicts, especially over water. With the collapse of most of these early civilisations, there has often been an accompanying forced reduction in population through starvation and/or disease.

We stand at a critical moment in Earth's history and we will choose its future. The Earth Charter outlines a vision of a sustainable global society founded on respect for Nature, universal human rights, economic justice and a culture of peace. We can either form a global partnership to care for the Earth and one another or risk our mutual destruction. It is an inspiring document, the spirit of which is reflected in the eight Millennium Development Goals set by the UN for 2015.

These goals would bring environmentally damaging activities under control and restore and protect the integrity of the Earth's systems we depend on. They would promote the management of resources like water and soil that are crucial to human welfare; reduce and eventually eliminate poverty; and promote sexual equality, giving women control over their own reproductive decisions and therefore help stabilise our population.

Implementation of these development goals would change the relationship between man and Nature. Implementing these policies would be enough to put civilisation on a sustainable path and re-engender hope instead of the projected decline and collapse – the inevitable result of our doing nothing.

Former Soviet statesman Mikhael Gorbachev told a story about two planets meeting in space. One looks ill and complains that it has contracted homo sapiens. The other planet is bursting with health and

169

responds: "Don't worry my friend. I had the same illness but it went away entirely of its own accord."

If you look at the last 50 years through the lenses of a conservation biologist and an economist, two very different pictures emerge: the dials and

Biologists are looking at the larger economy of life, while economists consider the sub-economy that humans have built by exploiting Nature.

gauges of the biologist show a worsening ecological situation on nearly all fronts. The economist, however, can point out that Gross World Product has increased by some 1300% in the last 100 years.

Biologists are looking at the larger economy of life, while economists consider the sub-economy that humans have built by exploiting Nature. The crux is this: nearly everywhere the larger economy of life itself is showing signs of stress and breakdown while the sub-economy is still expanding. We need to ask ourselves not whether one set of indicators is more accurate than the other, but rather which is more appropriate.

Using the best of both old and new technologies – from windmills to hydroponics – and crop rotation to genetic modification, we have a raft of solutions with which to restore the balance with Nature and sustainably increase the Earth's carrying capacity. Implementing sustainable policies means that at the very least we will no longer use up renewable resources faster than they can be replenished. We must invest in renewable technologies before non-renewable resources like oil begin to run out. We must recycle more and stop dumping rubbish into Nature at a faster rate than it can be absorbed.

Earth restoration science and entrepreneurialism will inspire people by showing ways in which we can repair the damage to ecosystems, restore natural capital and live in harmony with Nature without ditching our capitalist system. There are many thousands of great ideas being turned into environmental businesses every day as entrepreneurs view the environment as the next arena for success.

Politicians need to deliver financial incentives to encourage research and investment in these new technologies – such as renewable energy – instead of subsidising fossil fuels. They will also need to restructure the tax system to internalise environmental costs for existing businesses – from healthcare to pollution – that are currently externalised.

Then, more specific measures will be required to address the challenges we have outlined:

WATER – we will need to manage our water resources much more carefully, using 'more crop per drop' technology and working out where crops (including cotton) are best grown given the current distribution of water. We must manage the water cycle more rationally, harvesting rain where it falls. We will need to stop drawing down aquifers and start replenishing them through more integrated land management.

We also need to raise awareness of water use and water footprints, developing a 'water ethic'. Globally, water is becoming a commodity to be paid for and is no longer a right as it has been for many in wealthier nations.

LAND – we need to ban the use of salinated groundwater for irrigation – a tall order, but if we don't do this, then the affected ground may be barren for centuries. Restricting field size by planting hedges and creating ridges will help limit soil erosion as well as increase water supply as aquifers will replenish. Replanting of copses and trees especially along watercourses will prevent erosion and help mitigate climate change.

171

We need to restore soil quality by reducing nitrogen-based fertiliser usage and allowing the nematodes and natural soil composition to recover. We should institute a compulsory carbon offset programme for air travel and in due course for all use of fossil fuels – a forest re-planting tax.

THE SEAS – we need to stop overfishing and endangering species, ban disposal of by-catch, and create an effective, globally regulated and policed Mid-Ocean Treaty, sharing the resource of our seas sustainably. We need to live up to our existing commitments – the coastal nations agreed to create marine reserves that would cover 10% of the world's oceans by 2012. To date we have created reserves covering less than 1% of our seas. We also need to find ways of making fish farming sustainable – not destructive – through recycling our waste protein into useable protein.

POPULATION – we need to detach economic growth from environmental impact and devise new and viable measures of well-being and government leadership. The universal availability of family planning services has to be a core deliverable in our attempts to contain the rate of population increase. We have already seen the beneficial results in many countries, but over 200 million women worldwide still lack access to family planning services.

Our education systems must place an increasing emphasis on equipping young people with the necessary skills to compete in the new world economy. The current educational focus reflects the prioritisation of economics over ecology. Universities prize analytical thinking over a wider understanding of interconnected systems.

We need to develop the capacity to understand the ecological context in which we live, to recognise

Our existing educational system and focus simply equip people to be more effective vandals of the Earth.

limits, and to operate accordingly. Our task is to find ways of living within the resources of the planet, rather than expecting the planet to cater for our unlimited desires. Our existing educational system and focus simply equip people to be more effective vandals of the Earth. The increasing specialisation of knowledge means that most students graduate without any broad, integrated sense of the unity of things.

We need to redefine the concept of intelligence. Data is not knowledge and intelligence is more than cleverness. We cannot afford to become cleverer and less intelligent. We need to be educating the next generation to take action, something we have so far failed to accomplish. This involves an education of both head and heart, learning to know as well as to feel, balancing cleverness with wisdom.

Many people are fascinated by predictions of the future, but the fact is that we are creating our future every day. If you want to know what the future will bring, then just look at what we are doing now. Obviously there are imponderables, unpredictables and unimagined disasters – like the 2004 Indian Ocean tsunami and the 2011 Great East Japan earthquake and tsunami.

Extrapolating current trends, we can foresee that the pressure on food and commodity prices is likely to increase. The world is facing an emerging geopolitics of scarcity. This is already visible in the efforts by China and other developing countries to ensure access to its raw materials, oil supplies and land. The geopolitics of scarcity is an early manifestation of a civilisation outstripping its renewable environment and entering a collapse mode. Yet we still pursue our own short-term national and political interests as well as short-term profits, as if we were not part of a larger social and ecological system.

Meanwhile, our personal lives go on, but we can choose to engage in the sustainability revolution instead of just waiting for it to happen

173

to us. We can individually or collectively make a difference by becoming involved and choosing a particular issue about which we feel strongly. We can support one of the million of NGOs involved with environmental issues or involve ourselves in local politics and promote sustainability. We can change our consumption habits towards buying sustainable food and consumer products and support the companies that produce them.

Just because we can do only a little to make our planet better, it is not an excuse to do nothing. Similarly, just because we do a little doesn't mean it has no value. However serious the prospects for civilisation as a whole, we still have an individual responsibility to do something constructive, to take the next step towards a sustainable society, to rekindle some hope and encourage others to continue the process of healing our planet.

We must act now and start to repair our future.

175

BIBLIOGRAPHY

The following bibliography is not a definitive list of books and publications covering the concept of *The Protein Crunch*. Many newspapers, journals and magazines regularly publish articles and features on how we are damaging our planet.

Albritton, Robert. *Let Them Eat Junk,* London: Pluto Press, 2009.
Asubel, Kenny. *Nature's Operating Instructions,* San Francisco: Sierra Club, 2004.
Atkisson, Alan. *Believing Cassandra,* London: Earthscan, 1999, 2011.
Atkisson, Alan. *The Sustainability Transformation,* London: Earthscan, 2011.
Berry, Wendell. *Standing on Earth,* Cambridge: Golgonooza Press, 1991.
Bortoft, Henri. *The Wholeness of Nature - Goethe's Way of Science,* Edinburgh: Floris, 1996.
Boyle, David, Simms, Andrew. *The New Economics,* London: Earthscan, 2009.
Brand, Stewart. *Whole Earth Discipline,* New York: Viking, 2009.
Brooks, David B, Brandes, Oliver M, Gurman Stephen. *Making the Most of the Water We Have,* London: Earthscan, 2011.
Brown, Lester. *Who Will Feed China?* London: Earthscan, 1995.
Brown, Lester. *Tough Choices – facing the challenge of food security,* London: Earthscan, 1996.
Brown, Lester. *Eco-Economy,* New York: Norton, 2001.
Brown, Lester. *The Earth Policy Reader,* New York: Norton, 2002.
Brown, Lester. *Plan B 4.0,* New York: Norton, 2009.
Brown, Lester. *World on the Edge,* New York: Norton, 2011.
Campbell, T Colin, Campbell, Thomas M II. *The China Study,* New York: Benbella Books, 2005.
Capra, Fritjof. *The Web of Life,* London: HarperCollins, 1997.
Cato, Molly Scott. *Green Economics,* London: Earthscan, 2009.

Clarke, Robin, King, Jannett. *The Atlas of Water,* London: Earthscan, 2004.

Clover, Charles. *The End of the Line,* London: Ebury Press, 2004.

Clunies-Ross, Hildyard, Nicholas. *The Politics of Industrial Agriculture,* London: Earthscan, 1992.

Cohen, Joel. *How Many People Can the Earth Support?* New York: W.W.Norton, 1995.

COML. *Marine Census Highlights,* 2010.

Conford, Philip. *The Origins of the Organic Movement,* Edinburgh: Floris, 2001.

Connelly, James, Smith, Graham. *Politics and the Environment,* London: Routledge, 2003.

Dasgupta, Sir Partha. *Human Well-Being and the Natural Environment,* Oxford: Oxford University Press, 2001.

Delpeuch, Francis et al. *Globesity,* London: Earthscan, 2009.

Diamond, Jared. *Collapse,* London: Penguin, 2005.

D'Silva, Joyce, Webster, John. *The Meat Crisis,* London: Earthscan, 2011.

Ehrlich, Paul, Ehrlich, Anne. *The Population Explosion,* London: Hutchinson, 1990.

Ehrlich, Paul, Ehrlich, Anne. *Too Many People, Too Much Consumption,* Yale Environment 360 (www.e.360.yale.edu/) 2008.

Evanoff, Richard. *Bioregionalism and Global Ethics,* London: Routledge, 2010.

FAO. *The State of World Fisheries and Aquaculture,* 2008.

Farnish, Keith. *Time's Up,* Devon: Green Books, 2009.

Foresight, *The Future of Food and Farming,* London: UK Government report, 2011.

Foster, John. *The Sustainability Mirage,* London: Earthscan, 2008.

Friedman, Thomas L. *Hot, Flat and Crowded,* New York and London: Penguin, 2009.

Girardet, Herbert, Mondonca, Miguel. *A Renewable World,* Devon: Green Books, 2009.

Goldsmith, Edward. *The Way,* Devon: Green Books, 1996.

Goodwin, Brian. *Nature's Due,* Edinburgh: Floris Books, 2007.

Gore, Al. *Earth in the Balance,* London: Earthscan, 1992, 2008.

Grescoe, Taras. *Dead Seas,* London: Pan, 2008.

Hahlbrock, Klaus. *Feeding the Planet,* Frankfurt: Haus, 2007.

Hamilton, Clive. *Requiem for a Species,* London: Earthscan, 2010.

Hartmann, Thom. *The Last Hours of Ancient Sunlight,* London: Hodder
        & Stoughton, 1999.

Hawken, Paul. *Blessed Unrest,* London: Penguin, 2008.

Heinberg, Richard. *Peak Everything,* London: Clairview, 2008.

Henderson, Hazel. *Ethical Markets,* New York: Chelsea Green, 2006.

Herman, Patrick, Kuper, Richard. *Food for Thought,* London: Pluto
        Press, 2003.

Holgate, Sir Martin. *The Green Web,* London: Earthscan, 1999.

Houghton, Sir John. *Global Warming,* Cambridge: Cambridge
        University Press, 2004.

Howard, Sir Albert. *An Agricultural Testament,* London: Faber, 1945.

Howard, Sir Albert. *Farming and Gardening for Health or Disease,*
        London: Faber, 1945.

Hussen, Ahmed. *Principles of Environmental Economics,* London:
        Routledge, 2004.

Jackson, Tim. *Prosperity without Growth,* London: Earthscan, 2010.

Keller, David R. *Environmental Ethics,* Oxford: Wiley-Blackwell, 2010.

Kempf, Herve. *How the Rich are Destroying the Earth,* Devon: Green
        Books, 2008.

Kumar, Satish. *Earth Pilgrim,* Devon: Green Books, 2010.

L'Anson, Mark. *Scotland's East Coast Fishing Industry,* Stenlake
        Publishing, 2008.

Lang, Tim, Heasman, Michael. *Food Wars,* London: Earthscan, 2004.

Laszlo, Ervin. *The Chaos Point,* London: Piatkus, 2006.

Laszlo, Ervin. *Quantum Shift in the Global Brain,* Vermont: Inner
        Traditions, 2008.

Leonard, Annie. *The Story of Stuff,* London: Constable, 2010.

Lovelock, James. *The Revenge of Gaia*, London: Allen Lane, 2008

Lynas, Mark. *Six Degrees,* London: Harper, 2007.

Maclean, Charles. *The Fringe of Gold,* Edinburgh: Canongate, 1985.

Madeley, John. *Food for All,* London: Zed Books, 2002.

Mason, Colin. *A Short History of the Future,* London: Earthscan, 2006.

McIntosh, Alastair. *Hell and High Water,* London: Birlinn, 2008.

Meadows, Donella, Meadows, Dennis and Manders, Jorgen. *Beyond the Limits,* London: Earthscan, 1992.

Mumford, Lewis. *The Transformations of Man,* London: Allen and Unwin, 1957.

Myers, Adrian. *Organic Futures,* Devon: Green Books, 2006.

Myers, Norman. *Managing the Planet,* London: Earthscan, 2000.

Nasr, Seyyed Hossein. *Man and Nature,* London: Allen & Unwin, 1967.

Naydler, Jeremy. *Goethe on Science,* Edinburgh: Floris, 1996.

Nickerson, Raymond S. *Psychology and Environmental Change,* New York: Lawrence Erlbaum, 2003.

Orr, David. *Earth in Mind,* London: Island, 2004.

Osthaus, Karl-Ernst. *The Biodynamic Farm,* Edinburgh: Floris Books, 2010.

Parkin, Sara. *The Positive Deviant,* London: Earthscan, 2010.

Patel, Raj. *Stuffed and Starved,* London: Portobello, 2007.

Pauli, Gunter. *The Blue Economy,* New Mexico: Paradigm Publications, 2010.

Pearce, Fred. *When the Rivers Run Dry,* London: Transworld, 2006.

Pearce, Fred. *Peoplequake,* Eden Project Books, London: Transworld, 2010.

Pew Research Center. *The Future of the Global Muslim Population,* Projections for 2010-2030, 2011.

Porritt, Jonathon. *Capitalism as if the World Matters,* London: Earthscan, 2006.

Pretty, Jules. *The Living Land,* London: Earthscan, 1998.

Pretty, Jules. *Agri-Culture,* London: Earthscan, 2002.

Reich, Robert. *Supercapitalism,* London: Icon Books, 2009.

Roberts, Callum. *The Unnatural History of the Sea,* London: Gaia, 2007.

Roberts, Paul. *The End of Oil,* London: Bloomsbury, 2004.

Roberts, Paul. *The End of Food,* London: Bloomsbury, 2008.

Royal Society. *Population, The Complex Reality,* London: Royal
        Society, 1994.

Rubin, Jeff. *Why the World is about to get a Whole Lot Smaller,*
        London: Virgin, 2009.

Ryan, Anne B. *Enough is Plenty,* Hampshire: O Books, 2010.

Schauberger, Viktor. *Nature as Teacher,* Bath: Gateway Books, 1998.

Schauberger, Viktor. *The Fertile Earth,* Bath: Gateway Books, 2000.

Seamon, David, Zajonc, Arthur. *Goethe's Way of Science,* New York:
        SUNY, 1998.

Senge, Peter. *The Necessary Revolution,* Nicholas Brealey, London.

Smith, Peter (1985) *The Lammas Drave and the Winter Herrin,*
        Edinburgh: John Donald, 2010.

Smith, Peter. *The History of Steam and the East Fife Fishing Fleet,*
        Leven: James Corstorphine, 1998.

Starke, Linda (ed). *Vital Signs,* London: Earthscan, 1997-2000.

State of the World – annual series. Edition on *Innovations that Nourish
        the Planet,* London: Earthscan, 2011.

Stone, Michael, Barlow, Zenobia. *Ecological Literacy,* San Francisco:
        Sierra Club, 2005.

Stuart, Tristram. *Waste,* London: Penguin, 2009.

Tansey, Geoff, Worsley, Tony. *The Food System,* London: Earthscan,
        1995.

Tudge, Colin. *Feeding the World is Easy,* Italy: Pari Publishing, 2009.

Tudge, Colin. *Good Food for Everyone Forever,* Italy: Pari Publishing,
        2011.

UNFPA. *State of the World Population,* UN web site: 2009.

UN-HABITAT. *The Challenge of Slums,* UN web site: 2003.

Uphoff, Norman (ed). *Agroecological Innovations,* London: Earthscan,
        2002.

Wales, HRH the Prince of, with Skelly, Ian and Juniper, Tony. *Harmony*,
        London: *Blue Door,* 2010.

Walker, Gabrielle, King, Sir David. *The Hot Topic,* London: Bloomsbury,
        2008.

Weisman, Alan. *The World Without Us,* London: Virgin Books, 2008.

WEBSITES

The websites of the following organisations and individuals were particularly useful to *The Protein Crunch* research:

About My Planet – www.aboutmyplanet.com
Alternative Energy – www.alternative-energy-news.info/
Be the Change – www.bethechange.org.uk
Centre for Economic Performance – www.cep.lse.ac.uk
Center for Partnership Studies – www.partnershipway.org
Riane Eisler – www.rianeeisler.com
Club of Budapest – www.clubofbudapest.org
WorldShift Network – www.worldshiftnetwork.org
Earth Policy Institute – www.earth-policy.org
The Ecologist – www.theecologist.org
UN Food and Agriculture – www.fao.org
Forum for the Future – www.forumforthefuture.org
Friends of the Earth – www.foe.org
Greenpeace – www.greenpeace.org
Hazel Henderson – www.hazelhenderson.com
Institute of Noetic Sciences – www.noetic.org
International Futures Forum – www.internationalfuturesforum.com
New Economics Foundation – www.neweconomics.org
Resurgence Magazine – www.resurgence.org
Save Our Seas – www.saveourseas.com
Schumacher Society UK – www.schumachersociety.org.uk
Scientific and Medical Network – www.scimednet.org
Simultaneous Policy Association – www.simpol.org.uk
Soil Association – www.soilassociation.org
State of the World Forum – www.worldforum.org
Treehugger – www.treehugger.com
United Nations – www.un.org

Union of Concerned Scientists – www.ucsusa.org
World Future Council – www.worldfuturecouncil.org
World Health Organisation – www.who.int
World Bank – www.worldbank.org
ZERI – www.zeri.org

A more comprehensive list of research papers and their URL links are detailed in *The Protein Crunch* website: www.theproteincrunch.com/resources.html